WAIFS AND STRAYS

THE COMPLETE EDITION OF

O. Henry

WAIFS AND STRAYS

[V.2]

Garden City   New York
Doubleday, Doran & Company, Inc.

ACKNOWLEDGMENT

For permission to use material in this volume acknowledgment is due the Press Publishing Company, *Everybody's Magazine*, *Ainslee's Magazine*, *Hampton's Magazine*, the *Cosmopolitan*, the Macmillan Company, the John Lane Company, *Success*, the *Bookman*, the George Doran Company, Dodd, Mead and Company, *Current Literature*, and the *North American Review*.

CONTENTS

PART ONE

TWELVE STORIES

PART TWO

CRITICAL AND BIOGRAPHICAL COMMENT

By Arthur W. Page

CONTENTS

PART I
TWELVE STORIES

WAIFS AND STRAYS

THE RED ROSES OF TONIA

A TRESTLE burned down on the International Railroad. The south-bound from San Antonio was cut off for the next forty-eight hours. On that train was Tonia Weaver's Easter hat.

Espirition, the Mexican, who had been sent forty miles in a buckboard from the Espinosa Ranch to fetch it, returned with a shrugging shoulder and hands empty except for a cigarette. At the small station, Nopal, he had learned of the delayed train and, having no commands to wait, turned his ponies toward the ranch again.

Now, if one supposes that Easter, the Goddess of Spring, cares any more for the after-church parade on Fifth Avenue than she does for her loyal outfit of subjects that assemble at the meeting-house at Cactus, Tex., a mistake has been made. The wives and daughters of the ranchmen of the Frio country put forth Easter blossoms of new hats and gowns as faithfully as is done anywhere, and the Southwest is, for one day, a mingling of prickly pear, Paris, and paradise. And now it was Good Friday, and Tonia Weaver's Easter hat blushed unseen in the desert

3

air of an impotent express car, beyond the burned trestle. On Saturday noon the Rogers girls, from the Shoestring Ranch, and Ella Reeves, from the Anchor-O, and Mrs. Bennett and Ida, from Green Valley, would convene at the Espinosa and pick up Tonia. With their Easter hats and frocks carefully wrapped and bundled against the dust, the fair aggregation would then merrily jog the ten miles to Cactus, where on the morrow they would array themselves, sub-jugate man, do homage to Easter, and cause jealous agitation among the lilies of the field.

Tonia sat on the steps of the Espinosa ranch house flicking gloomily with a quirt at a tuft of curly mesquite. She displayed a frown and a contume-lious lip, and endeavoured to radiate an aura of dis-agreeableness and tragedy.

"I hate railroads," she announced positively. "And men. Men pretend to run them. Can you give any excuse why a trestle should burn? Ida Bennett's hat is to be trimmed with violets. I shall not go one step toward Cactus without a new hat. If I were a man I would get one."

Two men listened uneasily to this disparagement of their kind. One was Wells Pearson, foreman of the Mucho Calor cattle ranch. The other was Thompson Burrows, the prosperous sheepman from the Quintana Valley. Both thought Tonia Weaver adorable, especially when she railed at railroads and menaced men. Either would have given up his epidermis to make for her an Easter hat more cheerfully than the ostrich gives up his tip or the aigrette lays down its life. Neither possessed the ingenuity to conceive a means of supplying the sad deficiency against the coming Sabbath. Pearson's deep brown face and sunburned light hair gave him the appearance of a schoolboy seized by one of youth's profound and insolvable melancholies. Tonia's plight grieved him through and through. Thompson Burrows was the more skilled and pliable. He hailed from somewhere in the East originally; and he wore neckties and shoes, and was not made dumb by woman's presence.

"The big water-hole on Sandy Creek," said Pearson, scarcely hoping to make a hit, "was filled up by that last rain."

"Oh! Was it?" said Tonia sharply. "Thank you for the information. I suppose a new hat is nothing to you, Mr. Pearson. I suppose you think a woman ought to wear an old Stetson five years without a change, as you do. If your old water-hole could have put out the fire on that trestle you might have some reason to talk about it."

"I am deeply sorry," said Burrows, warned by Pearson's fate, "that you failed to receive your hat, Miss Weaver—deeply sorry, indeed. If there was anything I could do——"

"Don't bother," interrupted Tonia, with sweet sarcasm. "If there was anything you could do, you'd be doing it, of course. There isn't."

Tonia paused. A sudden sparkle of hope had come

into her eye. Her frown smoothed away. She had an inspiration.

"There's a store over at Lone Elm Crossing on the Nueces," she said, "that keeps hats. Eva Rogers got hers there. She said it was the latest style. They might have some left. But it's twenty-eight miles to Lone Elm."

The spurs of two men who hastily arose jingled; and Tonia almost smiled. The Knights, then, were not all turned to dust; nor were their rowels rust.

"Of course," said Tonia, looking thoughtfully at a white gulf cloud sailing across the cerulean dome, "nobody could ride to Lone Elm and back by the time the girls call by for me to-morrow. So, I reckon I'll have to stay at home this Easter Sunday."

And then she smiled.

"Well, Miss Tonia," said Pearson, reaching for his hat, as guileful as a sleeping babe. "I reckon I'll be trotting along back to Mucho Calor. There's some cutting out to be done on Dry Branch first thing in the morning; and me and Road Runner has got to be on hand. It's too bad your hat got sidetracked. Maybe they'll get that trestle mended yet in time for Easter."

"I must be riding, too, Miss Tonia," announced Burrows, looking at his watch. "I declare, it's nearly five o'clock! I must be out at my lambing camp in time to help pen those crazy ewes."

Tonia's suitors seemed to have been smitten with a need for haste. They bade her a ceremonious

6

farewell, and then shook each other's hands with the elaborate and solemn courtesy of the South-westerner.

"Hope I'll see you again soon, Mr. Pearson," said Burrows.

"Same here," said the cowman, with the serious face of one whose friend goes upon a whaling voy-age. "Be gratified to see you ride over to Mucho Calor any time you strike that section of the range."

Pearson mounted Road Runner, the soundest cow-pony on the Frio, and let him pitch for a minute, as be always did on being mounted, even at the end of a hard day's travel.

"What kind of a hat was that, Miss Tonia," he called, "that you ordered from San Antone? I can't help but be sorry about that hat."

"A straw," said Tonia; "the latest shape, of course; trimmed with red roses. That's what I like —red roses."

"There's no colour more becoming to your com-plexion and hair," said Burrows admiringly.

"It's what I like," said Tonia. "And of all the flowers, give me red roses. Keep all the pinks and blues for yourself. But what's the use, when tres-tles burn and leave you without anything? It'll be a dry old Easter for me!"

Pearson took off his hat and drove Road Runner at a gallop into chaparral east of the Espinosa ranch house.

As his stirrups rattled against the brush Burrows's

long-legged sorrel struck out down the narrow stretch of open prairie to the southwest.

Tonia hung up her quirt and went into the sitting-room.

"I'm mighty sorry, daughter, that you didn't get your hat," said her mother.

"Oh, don't worry, mother," said Tonia coolly. "I'll have a new hat, all right, in time to-morrow."

When Burrows reached the end of the strip of prairie he pulled his sorrel to the right and let him pick his way daintily across a sacuista flat through which ran the ragged, dry bed of an arroyo. Then up a gravelly hill, matted with bush, the horse scrambled, and at length emerged, with a snort of satisfaction, into a stretch of high, level prairie, grassy and dotted with the lighter green of mesquites in their fresh spring foliage. Always to the right Burrows bore, until in a little while he struck the old Indian trail that followed the Nueces southward, and that passed, twenty-eight miles to the southeast, through Lone Elm.

Here Burrows urged the sorrel into a steady lope. As he settled himself in the saddle for a long ride he heard the drumming of hoofs, the hollow "thwack" of chaparral against wooden stirrups, the whoop of a Comanche; and Wells Pearson burst out of the brush at the right of the trail like a precocious yellow chick from a dark green Easter egg.

Except in the presence of awing femininity, melancholy found no place in Pearson's bosom. In Tonia's presence his voice was as soft as a summer bullfrog's in his reedy nest. Now, at his gleesome yawp, rabbits, a mile away, ducked their ears, and sensitive plants closed their fearful fronds.

"Moved your lambing camp pretty far from the ranch, haven't you, neighbour?" asked Pearson, as Road Runner fell in at the sorrel's side.

"Twenty-eight miles," said Burrows, looking a little grim. Pearson's laugh woke an owl one hour too early in his water-elm on the river bank, half a mile away.

"All right for you, sheepman. I like an open game, myself. We're two locoed he-milliners hat-hunting in the wilderness. I notify you, Burr, to mind your corrals. We've got an even start; and the one that gets the headgear will stand some higher at the Espinosa."

"You've got a good pony," said Burrows, eyeing Road Runner's barrel-like body and tapering legs that moved as regularly as the piston-rod of an engine. "It's a race, of course; but you're too much of a horseman to whoop it up this soon. Say we travel together till we get to the home stretch."

"I'm your company," agreed Pearson, "and I admire your sense. If there's hats at Lone Elm, one of 'em shall set on Miss Tonia's brow to-morrow, and you won't be at the crowning. I ain't bragging, Burr, but that sorrel of yours is weak in the fore-legs."

"My horse against yours," offered Burrows, "that

9

Miss Tonia wears the hat I take her to Cactus to-morrow."

"I'll take you up," shouted Pearson. "But, oh, it's just like horse-stealing for me! I can use that sorrel for a lady's animal when—when somebody comes over to Mucho Calor, and——"

Burrows's dark face glowered so suddenly that the cowman broke off his sentence. But Pearson could never feel any pressure for long.

"What's all this Easter business about, Burr?" he asked cheerfully. "Why do the women folks have to have new hats by the almanac or bust all cinches trying to get 'em?"

"It's a seasonable statute out of the testaments," explained Burrows. "It's ordered by the Pope or somebody. And it has something to do with the Zodiac. I don't know exactly, but I think it was invented by the Egyptians."

"It's an all-right jubilee if the heathens did put their brand on it," said Pearson; "or else Tonia wouldn't have anything to do with it. And they pull it off at church, too. Suppose there ain't but one hat in the Lone Elm store, Burr!"

"Then," said Burrows, darkly, "the best man of us'll take it back to the Espinosa."

"Oh, man!" cried Pearson, throwing his hat high and catching it again, "there's nothing like you come off the sheep ranges before. You talk good and collateral to the occasion. And if there's more than one?"

"Then," said Burrows, "we'll pick our choice; and one of us'll get back first with his and the other won't."

"There never was two souls," proclaimed Pearson to the stars, "that beat more like one heart than yourn and mine. Me and you might be riding on a unicorn and thinking out of the same piece of mind."

At a little past midnight the riders loped into Lone Elm. The half a hundred houses of the village were dark. On its only street the big wooden store stood barred and shuttered.

In a few moments the horses were fastened and Pearson was pounding cheerfully on the door of old Sutton, the storekeeper.

The barrel of a Winchester came through a cranny of a solid window shutter, followed by a short inquiry.

"Wells Pearson, of the Mucho Calor, and Burrows, of Green Valley," was the response. "We want to buy some goods in the store. Sorry to wake you up, but we must have 'em. Come on out, Uncle Tommy, and get a move on you."

Uncle Tommy was slow, but at length they got him behind his counter with a kerosene lamp lit, and told him of their dire need.

"Easter hats?" said Uncle Tommy sleepily. "Why, yes, I believe I have got just a couple left. I only ordered a dozen this spring. I'll show 'em to you."

Now, Uncle Tommy Sutton was a merchant, half asleep or awake. In dusty pasteboard boxes under the counter he had two left-over spring hats. But, alas! for his commercial probity on that early Saturday noon—they were hats of two springs ago, and a woman's eye would have detected the fraud at half a glance. But to the unintelligent gaze of the cow-puncher and the sheepman they seemed fresh from the mint of contemporaneous April.

The hats were of a variety once known as "cart-wheels." They were of stiff straw, coloured red, and flat brimmed. Both were exactly alike, and trimmed lavishly around their crowns with full blown, immaculate, artificial white roses.

"That all you got, Uncle Tommy?" said Pearson. "All right. Not much choice here, Burr. Take your pick."

"They're the latest styles," lied Uncle Tommy. "You'd see 'em on Fifth Avenue, if you was in New York."

Uncle Tommy wrapped and tied each hat in two yards of dark calico for a protection. One Pearson tied carefully to his calfskin saddle-thongs; and the other became part of Road Runner's burden. They shouted thanks and farewells to Uncle Tommy, and cantered back into the night on the home stretch.

The horsemen jockeyed with all their skill. They rode more slowly on their way back. The few words they spoke were not unfriendly. Burrows had a Winchester under his left leg slung over his saddle horn. Pearson had a six-shooter belted around him. Thus men rode in the Frio country.

At half-past seven in the morning they rode to the top of a hill and saw the Espinosa Ranch, a white spot under a dark patch of live-oaks, five miles away.

The sight roused Pearson from his drooping pose in the saddle. He knew what Road Runner could do. The sorrel was lathered, and stumbling frequently. Road Runner was pegging away like a donkey engine.

Pearson turned toward the sheepman and laughed. "Good-bye, Burr," he cried, with a wave of his hand. "It's a race now. We're on the home stretch."

He pressed Road Runner with his knees and leaned toward the Espinosa. Road Runner struck into a gallop, with tossing head and snorting nostrils, as if he were fresh from a month in pasture.

Pearson rode twenty yards and heard the unmistakable sound of a Winchester lever throwing a cartridge into the barrel. He dropped flat along his horse's back before the crack of the rifle reached his ears.

It is possible that Burrows intended only to disable the horse—he was a good enough shot to do that without endangering his rider. But as Pearson stooped the ball went through his shoulder and then through Road Runner's neck. The horse fell and the cowman pitched over his head into the hard road, and neither of them tried to move.

Burrows rode on without stopping.

In two hours Pearson opened his eyes and took

inventory. He managed to get to his feet and staggered back to where Road Runner was lying.

Road Runner was lying there, but he appeared to be comfortable. Pearson examined him and found that the bullet had "creased" him. He had been knocked out temporarily, but not seriously hurt. But he was tired, and he lay there on Miss Tonia's hat and ate leaves from a mesquite branch that obligingly hung over the road.

Pearson made the horse get up. The Easter hat, loosed from the saddle-thongs, lay there in its calico wrappings, a shapeless thing from its sojourn beneath the solid carcass of Road Runner. Then Pearson fainted and fell headlong upon the poor hat again, crumpling it under his wounded shoulders.

It is hard to kill a cowpuncher. In half an hour he revived—long enough for a woman to have fainted twice and tried ice-cream for a restorer. He got up carefully and found Road Runner who was busy with the near-by grass. He tied the unfortunate hat to the saddle again, and managed to get himself there, too, after many failures.

At noon a gay and fluttering company waited in front of the Espinosa Ranch. The Rogers girls were there in their new buckboard, and the Anchor-O outfit, and the Green Valley folks—mostly women. And each and every one wore her new Easter hat, even upon the lonely prairies, for they greatly desired to shine forth and do honour to the coming festival.

At the gate stood Tonia, with undisguised tears

upon her cheeks. In her hand she held Burrows's Lone Elm hat, and it was at its white roses, hated by her, that she wept. For her friends were telling her, with the ecstatic joy of true friends, that cartwheels could not be worn, being three seasons passed into oblivion.

"Put on your old hat and come, Tonia," they urged.

"For Easter Sunday?" she answered. "I'll die first." And wept again.

The hats of the fortunate ones were curved and twisted into the style of spring's latest proclamation.

A strange being rode out of the brush among them, and there sat his horse languidly. He was stained and disfigured with the green of grass and the limestone of rocky roads.

"Hallo, Pearson," said Daddy Weaver. "Look like you've been breaking a mustang. What's that you've got tied to your saddle—a pig in a poke?"

"Oh, come on, Tonia, if you're going," said Betty Rogers. "We mustn't wait any longer. We've saved a seat in the buckboard for you. Never mind the hat. That lovely muslin you've got on looks sweet enough with any old hat."

Pearson was slowly untying the queer thing on his saddle. Tonia looked at him with a sudden hope. Pearson was a man who created hope. He got the thing loose and handed it to her. Her quick fingers tore at the strings.

"Best I could do," said Pearson slowly. "What

Road Runner and me done to it will be about all it needs."

"Oh, oh! it's just the right shape," shrieked Tonia. "And red roses! Wait till I try it on!"

She flew in to the glass, and out again, beaming, radiating, blossomed.

"Oh, don't red become her?" chanted the girls in recitative. "Hurry up, Tonia!"

Tonia stopped for a moment by the side of Road Runner.

"Thank you, thank you, Wells," she said happily. "It's just what I wanted. Won't you come over to Cactus to-morrow and go to church with me?"

"If I can," said Pearson. He was looking curiously at her hat, and then he grinned weakly.

Tonia flew into the buckboard like a bird. The vehicles sped away for Cactus.

"What have you been doing, Pearson?" asked Daddy Weaver. "You ain't looking so well as common."

"Me?" said Pearson. "I've been painting flowers. Them roses was white when I left Lone Elm. Help me down, Daddy Weaver, for I haven't got any more paint to spare."

ROUND THE CIRCLE*

F IND yo' shirt all right, Sam?" asked Mrs. Webber, from her chair under the live-oak, where she was comfortably seated with a paper-back volume for company.

"It balances perfeckly, Marthy," answered Sam, with a suspicious pleasantness in his tone. "At first I was about ter be a little reckless and kick 'cause ther buttons was all off, but since I diskiver that the button holes is all busted out, why, I wouldn't go so fur as to say the buttons is any loss to speak of."

"Oh, well," said his wife carelessly, "put on your necktie—that'll keep it together."

Sam Webber's sheep ranch was situated in the loneliest part of the country between the Nueces and the Frio. The ranch house—a two-room box structure—was on the rise of a gently swelling hill in the midst of a wilderness of high chaparral. In front of it was a small clearing where stood the sheep pens, shearing shed, and wool house. Only a few feet back of it began the thorny jungle.

Sam was going to ride over to the Chapman ranch to see about buying some more improved merino rams. At length he came out, ready for his ride.

---

*This story is especially interesting as an early treatment (1902) of the theme afterward developed with a surer hand in The Pendulum.

This being a business trip of some importance, and the Chapman ranch being almost a small town in population and size, Sam had decided to "dress up" accordingly. The result was that he had transformed himself from a graceful, picturesque frontiersman into something much less pleasing to the sight. The tight white collar awkwardly constricted his muscular, mahogany-coloured neck. The buttonless shirt bulged in stiff waves beneath his unbuttoned vest. The suit of "ready-made" effectually concealed the fine lines of his straight, athletic figure. His berry-brown face was set to the melancholy dignity befitting a prisoner of state. He gave Randy, his three-year-old son, a pat on the head, and hurried out to where Mexico, his favourite saddle horse, was standing.

Marthy, leisurely rocking in her chair, fixed her place in the book with her finger, and turned her head, smiling mischievously as she noted the havoc Sam had wrought with his appearance in trying to "fix up."

"Well, ef I must say it, Sam," she drawled, "you look jest like one of them hayseeds in the picture papers, 'stead of a free and independent sheepman of ther State o' Texas."

Sam climbed awkwardly into the saddle.

"You're the one ought to be 'shamed to say so," he replied hotly. "'Stead of 'tendin' to a man's clothes you're al'ays settin' around a'-readin them billy-by-dam yaller-back novils."

"Oh, shet up and ride along," said Mrs. Webber,

with a little jerk at the handles of her chair; "you al'ays fussin' 'bout my readin'. I do a-plenty; and I'll read when I wanter. I live in the bresh here like a varmint, never seein' nor hearin' nothin', and what other 'musement kin I have? Not in listenin' to you talk, for it's complain, complain, one day after another. Oh, go on, Sam, and leave me in peace."

Sam gave his pony a squeeze with his knees and "shoved" down the wagon trail that connected his ranch with the old, open Government road. It was eight o'clock, and already beginning to be very warm. He should have started three hours earlier. Chapman ranch was only eighteen miles away, but there was a road for only three miles of the distance. He had ridden over there once with one of the Half-Moon cowpunchers, and he had the direction well defined in his mind.

Sam turned off the old Government road at the split mesquite, and struck down the arroyo of the Quintanilla. Here was a narrow stretch of smiling valley, upholstered with a rich mat of green, curly mesquite grass; and Mexico consumed those few miles quickly with his long, easy lope. Again, upon reaching Wild Duck Waterhole, must he abandon well-defined ways. He turned now to his right up a little hill, pebble-covered, upon which grew only the tenacious and thorny prickly pear and chaparral. At the summit of this he paused to take his last general view of the landscape for, from now on, he must wind through brakes and thickets of chaparral, pear, and mesquite, for the most part seeing scarcely farther than twenty yards in any direction, choosing his way by the prairie-dweller's instinct, guided only by an occasional glimpse of a far-distant hilltop, a peculiarly shaped knot of trees, or the position of the sun.

Sam rode down the sloping hill and plunged into the great pear flat that lies between the Quintanilla and the Piedra.

In about two hours he discovered that he was lost. Then came the usual confusion of mind and the hurry to get somewhere. Mexico was anxious to redeem the situation, twisting with alacrity along the tortuous labyrinths of the jungle. At the moment his master's sureness of the route had failed his horse had divined the fact. There were no hills now that they could climb to obtain a view of the country. They came upon a few, but so dense and interlaced was the brush that scarcely could a rabbit penetrate the mass. They were in the great, lonely thicket of the Frio bottoms.

It was a mere nothing for a cattleman or a sheep-man to be lost for a day or a night. The thing often happened. It was merely a matter of missing a meal or two and sleeping comfortably on your saddle blankets on a soft mattress of mesquite grass. But in Sam's case it was different. He had never been away from his ranch at night. Marthy was afraid of the country—afraid of Mexicans, of snakes, of panthers, even of sheep. So he had never left her alone.

It must have been about four in the afternoon when

Sam's conscience awoke. He was limp and drenched, rather from anxiety than the heat or fatigue. Until now he had been hoping to strike the trail that led to the Frio crossing and the Chapman ranch. He must have crossed it at some dim part of it and ridden beyond. If so he was now something like fifty miles from home. If he could strike a ranch—a camp—any place where he could get a fresh horse and inquire the road, he would ride all night to get back to Marthy and the kid.

So, I have hinted, Sam was seized by remorse. There was a big lump in his throat as he thought of the cross words he had spoken to his wife. Surely it was hard enough for her to live in that horrible country without having to bear the burden of his abuse. He cursed himself grimly, and felt a sudden flush of shame that overglowed the summer heat as he remembered the many times he had flouted and railed at her because she had a liking for reading fiction.

"Ther only so'ce ov amusement ther po' gal's got," said Sam aloud, with a sob, which unaccustomed sound caused Mexico to shy a bit. "A-livin' with a sore-headed kiote like me—a low-down skunk that ought to be licked to death with a saddle cinch—a-cookin' and a-washin' and a-livin' on mutton and beans—and me abusin' her fur takin' a squint or two in a little book!"

He thought of Marthy as she had been when he first met her in Dogtown—smart, pretty, and saucy

—before the sun had turned the roses in her cheeks brown and the silence of the chaparral had tamed her ambitions.

"Ef I ever speaks another hard word to ther little gal," muttered Sam, "or fails in the love and affection that's comin' to her in the deal, I hopes a wildcat 'll t'ar me to pieces."

He knew what he would do. He would write to Garcia & Jones, his San Antonio merchants where he bought his supplies and sold his wool, and have them send down a big box of novels and reading matter for Marthy. Things were going to be different. He wondered whether a little piano could be placed in one of the rooms of the ranch house without the family having to move out of doors.

In nowise calculated to allay his self-reproach was the thought that Marthy and Randy would have to pass that night alone. In spite of their bickerings, when night came Marthy was wont to dismiss her fears of the country, and rest her head upon Sam's strong arm with a sigh of peaceful content and dependence. And were her fears so groundless? Sam thought of roving, marauding Mexicans, of stealthy cougars that sometimes invaded the ranches, of rattlesnakes, centipedes, and a dozen possible dangers. Marthy would be frantic with fear. Randy would cry, and call for "dada" to come.

Still the interminable succession of stretches of brush, cactus, and mesquite. Hollow after hollow, slope after slope—all exactly alike—all familiar by constant repetition, and yet all strange and new. If he could only arrive *somewhere*.

The straight line is Art. Nature moves in circles. A straightforward man is more an artificial product than a diplomatist is. Men lost in the snow travel in exact circles until they sink, exhausted, as their footprints have attested. Also, travellers in philosophy and other mental processes frequently wind up at their starting-point.

It was when Sam Webber was fullest of contrition and good resolves that Mexico, with a heavy sigh, subsided from his regular, brisk trot into a slow, complacent walk. They were winding up an easy slope covered with brush ten or twelve feet high.

"I say now, Mex," demurred Sam, "this here won't do. I know you're plumb tired out, but we got ter git along. Oh, Lordy, ain't there no mo' houses in the world!" He gave Mexico a smart kick with his heels.

Mexico gave a protesting grunt as if to say: "What's the use of that, now we're so near?" He quickened his gait into a languid trot. Rounding a great clump of black chaparral, he stopped short. Sam dropped the bridle reins and sat, looking into the back door of his own house, not ten yards away.

Marthy, serene and comfortable, sat in her rocking-chair before the door in the shade of the house, with her feet resting luxuriously upon the steps. Randy, who was playing with a pair of spurs on the ground, looked up for a moment at his father and went on spinning the rowels and singing a little song. Marthy turned her head lazily against the back of the chair and considered the arrivals with emotionless eyes. She held a book in her lap with her finger holding the place.

Sam shook himself queerly, like a man coming out of a dream, and slowly dismounted. He moistened his dry lips.

"I see you are still a-settin'," he said, "a-readin' of them billy-by-dam yaller-back novils."

Sam had travelled round the circle and was himself again.

THE RUBBER PLANT'S STORY

WE RUBBER plants form the connecting link between the vegetable kingdom and the decorations of a Waldorf-Astoria scene in a Third Avenue theatre. I haven't looked up our family tree, but I believe we were raised by grafting a gum overshoe on to a 30-cent table d'hôte stalk of asparagus. You take a white bulldog with a Bourke Cockran air of independence about him and a rubber plant and there you have the fauna and flora of a flat. What the shamrock is to Ireland the rubber plant is to the dweller in flats and furnished rooms. We get moved from one place to another so quickly that the only way we can get our picture taken is with a kinetoscope. We are the vagrant vine and the flitting fig tree. You know the proverb: "Where the rubber plant sits in the window the moving van draws up to the door."

We are the city equivalent to the woodbine and the honeysuckle. No other vegetable except the Pittsburg stogie can withstand as much handling as we can. When the family to which we belong moves into a flat they set us in the front window and we become lares and penates, fly-paper and the peripatetic emblem of "Home Sweet Home." We aren't as green as we look. I guess we are about what you would call the soubrettes of the conservatory. You try sitting in the front window of a $40 flat in Manhattan and looking out into the street all day, and back into the flat at night, and see whether you get wise or not—hey? Talk about the tree of knowledge of good and evil in the garden of Eden—say! suppose there had been a rubber plant there when Eve—but I was going to tell you a story.

The first thing I can remember I had only three leaves and belonged to a member of the pony ballet. I was kept in a sunny window, and was generally watered with seltzer and lemon. I had plenty of fun in those days. I got cross-eyed trying to watch the numbers of the automobiles in the street and the dates on the labels inside at the same time.

Well, then the angel that was moulting for the musical comedy lost his last feather and the company broke up. The ponies trotted away and I was left in the window ownerless. The janitor gave me to a refined comedy team on the eighth floor, and in six weeks I had been set in the window of five different flats. I took on experience and put out two more leaves.

Miss Carruthers, of the refined comedy team—did you ever see her cross both feet back of her neck?—gave me to a friend of hers who had made an unfortunate marriage with a man in a store. Consequently I was placed in the window of a furnished room, rent in advance, water two flights up, gas extra after ten o'clock at night. Two of my leaves withered off here. Also, I was moved from one room to another so many times that I got to liking the odour of the pipes the expressmen smoked.

I don't think I ever had so dull a time as I did with this lady. There was never anything amusing going on inside—she was devoted to her husband, and, besides leaning out the window and flirting with the iceman, she never did a thing toward breaking the monotony.

When the couple broke up they left me with the rest of their goods at a second-hand store. I was put out in front for sale along with the jobbiest lot you ever heard of being lumped into one bargain. Think of this little cornucopia of wonders, all for $1.89: Henry James's works, six talking machine records, one pair of tennis shoes, two bottles of horse radish, and a rubber plant—that was me!

One afternoon a girl came along and stopped to look at me. She had dark hair and eyes, and she looked slim, and sad around the mouth.

"Oh, oh!" she says to herself. "I never thought to see one up here."

She pulls out a little purse about as thick as one of my leaves and fingers over some small silver in it. Old Koen, always on the lookout, is ready, rubbing his hands. This girl proceeds to turn down Mr. James and the other commodities. Rubber plants or nothing is the burden of her song. And at last Koen and she come together at 39 cents, and away she goes with me in her arms.

She was a nice girl, but not my style. Too quiet and sober looking. Thinks I to myself: "I'll just about land on the fire-escape of a tenement, six stories up. And I'll spend the next six months looking at clothes on the line."

But she carried me to a nice little room only three flights up in quite a decent street. And she put me in the window, of course. And then she went to work and cooked dinner for herself. And what do you suppose she had? Bread and tea and a little dab of jam! Nothing else. Not a single lobster, nor so much as one bottle of champagne. The Carruthers comedy team had both every evening, except now and then when they took a notion for pig's knuckle and kraut.

After she had finished her dinner my new owner came to the window and leaned down close to my leaves and cried softly to herself for a while. It made me feel funny. I never knew anybody to cry that way over a rubber plant before. Of course, I've seen a few of 'em turn on the tears for what they could get out of it, but she seemed to be crying just for the pure enjoyment of it. She touched my leaves like she loved 'em, and she bent down her head and kissed each one of 'em. I guess I'm about the toughest specimen of a peripatetic orchid on earth, but I tell you it made me feel sort of queer. Home never was like that to me before. Generally I used to get chewed by poodles and have shirt-waists hung on me to dry, and get watered with coffee grounds and peroxide of hydrogen.

This girl had a piano in the room, and she used to disturb it with both hands while she made noises with her mouth for hours at a time. I suppose she was practising vocal music.

One day she seemed very much excited and kept looking at the clock. At eleven somebody knocked and she let in a stout, dark man with towsled black hair. He sat down at once at the piano and played while she sang for him. When she finished she laid one hand on her bosom and looked at him. He shook his head, and she leaned against the piano.

"Two years already," she said, speaking slowly— "do you think in two more—or even longer?"

The man shook his head again. "You waste your time," he said, roughly I thought. "The voice is not there." And then he looked at her in a peculiar way. "But the voice is not everything," he went on. "You have looks. I can place you, as I told you if——"

The girl pointed to the door without saying anything, and the dark man left the room. And then she came over and cried around me again. It's a good thing I had enough rubber in me to be waterproof.

About that time somebody else knocked at the door. "Thank goodness," I said to myself. "Here's a chance to get the water-works turned off. I hope it's somebody that's game enough to stand a bird and a bottle to liven things up a little. Tell you the truth, this little girl made me tired. A rubber plant likes to see a little sport now and then. I don't suppose there's another green thing in New York that sees as much of gay life unless it's the chartreuse or the sprigs of parsley around the dish."

When the girl opens the door in steps a young chap in a travelling cap and picks her up in his arms, and she sings out "Oh, Dick!" and stays there long enough to—well, you've been a rubber plant, too, sometimes, I suppose.

"Good thing!" says I to myself. "This is livelier than scales and weeping. Now there'll be something doing."

"You've got to go back with me," says the young man. "I've come two thousand miles for you. Aren't you tired of it yet, Bess? You've kept all of us waiting so long. Haven't you found out yet what is best?"

"The bubble burst only to-day," says the girl. "Come here, Dick, and see what I found the other day on the sidewalk for sale." She brings him by the hand and exhibits yours truly. "How one ever got away up here who can tell? I bought it with almost the last money I had."

He looked at me, but he couldn't keep his eyes off her for more than a second.

"Do you remember the night, Bess," he said, "when we stood under one of those on the bank of the bayou and what you told me then?"

"Geewillikins!" I said to myself. "Both of them

stand under a rubber plant! Seems to me they are
stretching matters somewhat."

"Do I not," says she, looking up at him and sneak-
ing close to his vest, "and now I say it again, and
it is to last forever. Look, Dick, at its leaves, how
wet they are. Those are my tears, and it was thinking of you that made them fall."

"The dear old magnolias!" says the young man,
pinching one of my leaves. "I love them all."

Magnolia! Well, wouldn't that—say! those innocents thought I was a magnolia! What the—well,
wasn't that tough on a genuine little old New York
rubber plant?

OUT OF NAZARETH

O KOCHEE, in Georgia, had a boom, and J.
Pinkney Bloom came out of it with a "wad."
Okochee came out of it with a half-million-
dollar debt, a two and a half per cent. city property
tax, and a city council that showed a propensity for
travelling the back streets of the town. These things
came about through a fatal resemblance of the river
Cooloosa to the Hudson, as set forth and expounded
by a Northern tourist. Okochee felt that New York
should not be allowed to consider itself the only al-
ligator in the swamp, so to speak. And then that
harmless, but persistent, individual so numerous in
the South—the man who is always clamouring for
more cotton mills, and is ready to take a dollar's
worth of stock, provided he can borrow the dollar—
that man added his deadly work to the tourist's
innocent praise, and Okochee fell.

The Cooloosa River winds through a range of small
mountains, passes Okochee, and then blends its waters
trippingly, as fall the mellifluous Indian syllables
with the Chattahoochee.

Okochee rose, as it were, from its sunny seat on the
post-office stoop, hitched up its suspender, and threw
a granite dam two hundred and forty feet long and
sixty feet high across the Cooloosa one mile above the

32

town. Thereupon, a dimpling, sparkling lake backed up twenty miles among the little mountains. Thus in the great game of municipal rivalry did Okochee match that famous drawing card, the Hudson. It was conceded that nowhere could the Palisades be judged superior in the way of scenery and grandeur. Following the picture card was played the ace of commercial importance. Fourteen thousand horsepower would this dam furnish. Cotton mills, factories, and manufacturing plants would rise up as the green corn after a shower. The spindle and the fly-wheel and turbine would sing the shrewd glory of Okochee. Along the picturesque heights above the lake would rise in beauty the costly villas and the splendid summer residences of capital. The naphtha launch of the millionaire would spit among the romantic coves; the verdured hills would take formal shapes of terrace, lawn, and park. Money would be spent like water in Okochee, and water would be turned into money.

The fate of the good town is quickly told. Capital decided not to invest. Of all the great things promised, the scenery alone came to fulfilment. The wooded peaks, the impressive promontories of solemn granite, the beautiful green slants of bank and ravine did all they could to reconcile Okochee to the delinquency of miserly gold. The sunsets gilded the dreamy draws and coves with a minting that should charm away heart-burning. Okochee, true to the instinct of its blood and clime, was lulled by the spell.

It climbed out of the arena, loosed its suspender, sat down again on the post-office stoop, and took a chew. It consoled itself by drawling sarcasms at the city council which was not to blame, causing the fathers, as has been said, to seek back streets and figure perspiringly on the sinking fund and the appropriation for interest due.

The youth of Okochee—they who were to carry into the rosy future the burden of the debt—accepted failure with youth's uncalculating joy. For, here was sport, aquatic and nautical, added to the meagre round of life's pleasures. In yachting caps and flowing neckties they pervaded the lake to its limits. Girls wore silk waists embroidered with anchors in blue and pink. The trousers of the young men widened at the bottom, and their hands were proudly calloused by the oft-plied oar. Fishermen were under the spell of a deep and tolerant joy. Sailboats and rowboats furrowed the lenient waves, popcorn and ice-cream booths sprang up about the little wooden pier. Two small excursion steamboats were built, and plied the delectable waters. Okochee philosophically gave up the hope of eating turtle soup with a gold spoon, and settled back, not ill content, to its regular diet of lotus and fried hominy. And out of this slow wreck of great expectations rose up J. Pinkney Bloom with his "wad" and his prosperous, cheery smile.

Needless to say J. Pinkney was no product of Georgia soil. He came out of that flushed and capable region known as the "North." He called himself a "promoter"; his enemies had spoken of him as a "grafter"; Okochee took a middle course, and held him to be no better nor no worse than a "Yank."

Far up the lake—eighteen miles above the town— the eye of this cheerful camp-follower of booms had spied out a graft. He purchased there a precipitous tract of five hundred acres at forty-five cents per acre; and this he laid out and subdivided as the city of Skyland—the Queen City of the Switzerland of the South. Streets and avenues were surveyed; parks designed; corners of central squares reserved for the "proposed" opera house, board of trade, lyceum, market, public schools, and "Exposition Hall." The price of lots ranged from five to five hundred dollars. Positively, no lot would be priced higher than five hundred dollars.

While the boom was growing in Okochee, J. Pink- ney's circulars, maps, and prospectuses were flying through the mails to every part of the country. In- vestors sent in their money by post, and the Skyland Real Estate Company (J. Pinkney Bloom) returned to each a deed, duly placed on record, to the best lot, at the price, on hand that day. All this time the catamount screeched upon the reserved lot of the Skyland Board of Trade, the opossum swung by his tail over the site of the exposition hall, and the owl hooted a melancholy recitative to his audience of young squirrels in opera house square. Later, when the money was coming in fast, J. Pinkney caused to be erected in the coming city half a dozen cheap box houses, and persuaded a contingent of indigent natives to occupy them, thereby assuming the rôle of "population" in subsequent prospectuses, which became, accordingly, more seductive and remunerative.

So, when the dream faded and Okochee dropped back to digging bait and nursing its two and a half per cent. tax, J. Pinkney Bloom (unloving of checks and drafts and the cold interrogatories of bankers) strapped about his fifty-two-inch waist a soft leather belt containing eight thousand dollars in big bills, and said that all was very good.

One last trip he was making to Skyland before departing to other salad fields. Skyland was a regular post-office, and the steamboat, *Dixie Belle*, under contract, delivered the mail bag (generally empty) twice a week. There was a little business there to be settled—the postmaster was to be paid off for his light but lonely services, and the "inhabitants" had to be furnished with another month's homely rations, as per agreement. And then Skyland would know J. Pinkney Bloom no more. The owners of these precipitous, barren, useless lots might come and view the scene of their invested credulity, or they might leave them to their fit tenants, the wild hog and the browsing deer. The work of the Skyland Real Estate Company was finished.

The little steamboat *Dixie Belle* was about to shove

off on her regular up-the-lake trip, when a rickety
hired carriage rattled up to the pier, and a tall,
elderly gentleman, in black, stepped out, signalling
courteously but vivaciously for the boat to wait.
Time was of the least importance in the schedule of
the *Dixie Belle;* Captain MacFarland gave the order,
and the boat received its ultimate two passengers.
For, upon the arm of the tall, elderly gentleman,
as he crossed the gangway, was a little elderly lady,
with a gray curl depending quaintly forward of her
left ear.

Captain MacFarland was at the wheel; therefore
it seemed to J. Pinkney Bloom, who was the only
other passenger, that it should be his to play the
part of host to the boat's new guests, who were,
doubtless, on a scenery-viewing expedition. He
stepped forward, with that translucent, child-candid
smile upon his fresh, pink countenance, with that air
of unaffected sincerity that was redeemed from bluff-
ness only by its exquisite calculation, with that
promptitude and masterly decision of manner that
so well suited his calling—with all his stock in trade
well to the front, he stepped forward to receive
Colonel and Mrs. Peyton Blaylock. With the grace
of a grand marshal or a wedding usher, he escorted
the two passengers to a side of the upper deck, from
which the scenery was supposed to present itself to
the observer in increased quantity and quality. There,
in comfortable steamer chairs, they sat and began
to piece together the random lines that were to form

an intelligent paragraph in the big history of little events.

"Our home, sir," said Colonel Blaylock, removing his wide-brimmed, rather shapeless black felt hat, "is in Holly Springs—Holly Springs, Georgia. I am very proud to make your acquaintance, Mr. Bloom. Mrs. Blaylock and myself have just arrived in Okochee this morning, sir, on business—business of importance in connection with the recent rapid march of progress in this section of our state."

The Colonel smoothed back, with a sweeping gesture, his long, smooth, gray locks. His dark eyes, still fiery under the heavy, black brows, seemed inappropriate to the face of a business man. He looked rather to be an old courtier handed down from the reign of Charles, and reattired in a modern suit of fine, but ravelling and seam-worn, broadcloth.

"Yes, sir," said Mr. Bloom, in his heartiest prospectus voice, "things have been whizzing around Okochee. Biggest industrial revival and waking up to natural resources Georgia ever had. Did you happen to squeeze in on the ground floor in any of the gilt-edged grafts, Colonel?"

"Well, sir," said the Colonel, hesitating in courteous doubt, "if I understand your question, I may say that I took the opportunity to make an investment that I believe will prove quite advantageous—yes, sir, I believe it will result in both pecuniary profit and agreeable occupation."

"Colonel Blaylock," said the little elderly lady,

shaking her gray curl and smiling indulgent explanation at J. Pinkney Bloom, "is so devoted to business. He has such a talent for financiering and mar-
kets and investments and those kind of things. I
think myself extremely fortunate in having secured
him for a partner on life's journey—I am so unversed
in those formidable but very useful branches of
learning."

Colonel Blaylock rose and made a bow—a bow
that belonged with silk stockings and lace ruffles and
velvet.

"Practical affairs," he said, with a wave of his
hand toward the promoter, "are, if I may use the
comparison, the garden walks upon which we tread
through life, viewing upon either side of us the flowers which brighten that journey. It is my pleasure
to be able to lay out a walk or two. Mrs. Blaylock,
sir, is one of those fortunate higher spirits whose
mission it is to make the flowers grow. Perhaps,
Mr. Bloom, you have perused the lines of Lorella, the
Southern poetess. That is the name above which
Mrs. Blaylock has contributed to the press of the
South for many years."

"Unfortunately," said Mr. Bloom, with a sense of
the loss clearly written upon his frank face, "I'm
like the Colonel—in the walk-making business myself—and I haven't had time to even take a sniff
at the flowers. Poetry is a line I never dealt in. It
must be nice, though—quite nice."

"It is the region," smiled Mrs. Blaylock, "in

which my soul dwells. My shawl, Peyton, if you please—the breeze comes a little chilly from yon verdured hills."

The Colonel drew from the tail pocket of his coat a small shawl of knitted silk and laid it solicitously about the shoulders of the lady. Mrs. Blaylock sighed contentedly, and turned her expressive eyes—still as clear and unworldly as a child's—upon the steep slopes that were slowly slipping past. Very fair and stately they looked in the clear morning air. They seemed to speak in familiar terms to the responsive spirit of Lorella. "My native hills!" she murmured dreamily. "See how the foliage drinks the sunlight from the hollows and dells."

"Mrs. Blaylock's maiden days," said the Colonel, interpreting her mood to J. Pinkney Bloom, "were spent among the mountains of northern Georgia. Mountain air and mountain scenery recall to her those days. Holly Springs, where we have lived for twenty years, is low and flat. I fear that she may have suffered in health and spirits by so long a residence there. That is one potent reason for the change we are making. My dear, can you not recall those lines you wrote—entitled, I think, 'The Georgia Hills'—the poem that was so extensively copied by the Southern press and praised so highly by the Atlanta critics?"

Mrs. Blaylock turned a glance of speaking tenderness upon the Colonel, fingered for a moment the silvery curl that drooped upon her bosom, then looked again toward the mountains. Without preliminary or affectation or demurral she began, in rather thrilling and more deeply pitched tones to recite these lines:

"The Georgia hills, the Georgia hills!—
    Oh, heart, why dost thou pine?
Are not these sheltered lowlands fair
    With mead and bloom and vine?
Ah! as the slow-paced river here
    Broods on its natal rills
My spirit drifts, in longing sweet,
    Back to the Georgia hills

"And through the close-drawn, curtained night
    I steal on sleep's slow wings
Back to my heart's ease—slopes of pine—
    Where end my wanderings.
Oh, heaven seems nearer from their tops—
    And farther earthly ills—
Even in dreams, if I may but
    Dream of my Georgia hills.

The grass upon their orchard sides
    Is a fine couch to me;
The common note of each small bird
    Passes all minstrelsy.
It would not seem so dread a thing
    If, when the Reaper wills,
He might come there and take my hand
    Up in the Georgia hills."

"That's great stuff, ma'am," said J. Pinkney Bloom, enthusiastically, when the poetess had concluded. "I wish I had looked up poetry more than I have. I was raised in the pine hills myself."

"The mountains ever call to their children," murmured Mrs. Blaylock. "I feel that life will take on the rosy hue of hope again in among these beautiful hills. Peyton—a little taste of the currant wine, if you will be so good. The journey, though delightful in the extreme, slightly fatigues me."

Colonel Blaylock again visited the depths of his prolific coat, and produced a tightly corked, rough, black bottle. Mr. Bloom was on his feet in an instant. "Let me bring a glass, ma'am. You come along, Colonel—there's a little table we can bring, too. Maybe we can scare up some fruit or a cup of tea on board. I'll ask Mac."

Mrs. Blaylock reclined at ease. Few royal ladies have held their royal prerogative with the serene grace of the petted Southern woman. The Colonel, with an air as gallant and assiduous as in the days of his courtship, and J. Pinkney Bloom, with a ponderous agility half professional and half directed by some resurrected, unnamed, long-forgotten sentiment, formed a diversified but attentive court. The currant wine—wine home made from the Holly Springs fruit—went round; and then J. Pinkney began to hear something of Holly Springs life.

It seemed (from the conversation of the Blaylocks) that the Springs was decadent. A third of the population had moved away. Business—and the Colonel was an authority on business—had dwindled to nothing. After carefully studying the field of opportunities open to capital he had sold his little property there for eight hundred dollars, and invested it in one of the enterprises opened up by the book in Okochee.

"Might I inquire, sir," said Mr. Bloom, "in what particular line of business you inserted your coin? I know that town as well as I know the regulations for illegal use of the mails. I might give you a hunch as to whether you can make the game go or not."

J. Pinkney, somehow, had a kindly feeling toward these unsophisticated representatives of by-gone days. They were so simple, impractical, and unsuspecting. He was glad that he happened not to have a gold brick or a block of that western Bad Boy Silver Mine stock along with him. He would have disliked to unload on people he liked so well as he did these; but there are some temptations too enticing to be resisted.

"No, sir," said Colonel Blaylock, pausing to arrange the queen's wrap. "I did not invest in Okochee. I have made an exhaustive study of business conditions, and I regard old settled towns as unfavourable fields in which to place capital that is limited in amount. Some months ago, through the kindness of a friend, there came into my hands a map and description of this new town of Skyland that has been built upon the lake. The description was so pleasing, the future of the town set forth in such convincing arguments, and its increasing prosperity portrayed in such an attractive style that I decided to take advantage of the opportunity it offered. I carefully selected a lot in the centre of the business district, although its price was the highest in the schedule—five hundred dollars—and made the purchase at once."

"Are you the man—I mean, did you pay five hundred dollars for a lot in Skyland?" asked J. Pinkney Bloom.

"I did, sir," answered the Colonel, with the air of a modest millionaire explaining his success; "a lot most excellently situated on the same square with the opera house, and only two squares from the board of trade. I consider the purchase a most fortuitous one. It is my intention to erect a small building upon it at once, and open a modest book and stationery store. During past years I have met with many pecuniary reverses, and I now find it necessary to engage in some commercial occupation that will furnish me with a livelihood. The book and stationery business, though an humble one, seems to me not inapt nor altogether uncongenial. I am a graduate of the University of Virginia; and Mrs. Blaylock's really wonderful acquaintance with belles-lettres and poetic literature should go far toward insuring success. Of course, Mrs. Blaylock would not personally serve behind the counter. With the nearly three hundred dollars I have remaining I can manage the building of a house, by giving a lien on the lot. I have an old friend in Atlanta who is a partner in a large book store, and he has agreed to furnish me with a stock of goods on credit, on extremely easy terms. I am pleased to hope, sir, that Mrs. Blaylock's health and happiness will be increased by the change of locality. Already I fancy I can perceive the return of those roses that were once the hope and despair of Georgia cavaliers."

Again followed that wonderful bow, as the Colonel lightly touched the pale cheek of the poetess. Mrs. Blaylock, blushing like a girl, shook her curl and gave the Colonel an arch, reproving tap. Secret of eternal youth—where art thou? Every second the answer comes—"Here, here, here." Listen to thine own heart-beats, O weary seeker after external miracles.

"Those years," said Mrs. Blaylock, "in Holly Springs were long, long, long. But now is the promised land in sight. Skyland!—a lovely name."

"Doubtless," said the Colonel, "we shall be able to secure comfortable accommodations at some modest hotel at reasonable rates. Our trunks are in Okochee, to be forwarded when we shall have made permanent arrangements."

J. Pinkney Bloom excused himself, went forward, and stood by the captain at the wheel.

"Mac," said he, "do you remember my telling you once that I sold one of those five-hundred-dollar lots in Skyland?"

"Seems I do," grinned Captain MacFarland.

"I'm not a coward, as a general rule," went on the promoter. "but I always said that if I ever met

45

the sucker that bought that lot I'd run like a turkey.
Now, you see that old babe-in-the-wood over there?
Well, he's the boy that drew the prize. That was the
only five-hundred-dollar lot that went. The rest
ranged from ten dollars to two hundred. His wife
writes poetry. She's invented one about the high
grounds of Georgia, that's way up in G. They're
going to Skyland to open a book store."

"Well," said MacFarland, with another grin, "it's
a good thing you are along, J. P.; you can show 'em
around town until they begin to feel at home."

"He's got three hundred dollars left to build a
house and store with," went on J. Pinkney, as if he
were talking to himself. "And he thinks there's an
opera house up there."

Captain MacFarland released the wheel long enough
to give his leg a roguish slap.

"You old fat rascal!" he chuckled, with a wink.

"Mac, you're a fool," said J. Pinkney Bloom coldly.
He went back and joined the Blaylocks, where he
sat, less talkative, with that straight furrow between
his brows that always stood as a signal of schemes
being shaped within.

"There's a good many swindles connected with
these booms," he said presently. "What if this Skyland should turn out to be one—that is, suppose
business should be sort of dull there, and no special
sale for books?"

"My dear sir," said Colonel Blaylock, resting his
hand upon the back of his wife's chair, "three times

I have been reduced to almost penury by the duplicity of others, but I have not yet lost faith in humanity. If I have been deceived again, still we may glean health and content, if not worldly profit. I am aware that there are dishonest schemers in the world who set traps for the unwary, but even they are not altogether bad. My dear, can you recall those verses entitled, 'He Giveth the Increase,' that you composed for the choir of our church in Holly Springs?''

"That was four years ago," said Mrs. Blaylock; "perhaps I can repeat a verse or two.

> "The lily springs from the rotting mould;
>   Pearls from the deep sea slime;
> Good will come out of Nazareth
>   All in God's own time.
>
> "To the hardest heart the softening grace
>   Cometh, at last, to bless;
> Guiding it right to help and cheer
>   And succour in distress.

"I cannot remember the rest. The lines were not ambitious. They were written to the music composed by a dear friend."

"It's a fine rhyme, just the same," declared Mr. Bloom. "It seems to ring the bell, all right. I guess I gather the sense of it. It means that the rankest kind of a phony will give you the best end of it once in a while."

Mr. Bloom strayed thoughtfully back to the captain, and stood, meditating.

"Ought to be in sight of the spires and gilded

domes of Skyland now in a few minutes," chirruped MacFarland, shaking with enjoyment.

"Go to the devil," said Mr. Bloom, still pensive.

And now, upon the left bank, they caught a glimpse of a white village, high up on the hills, smothered among green trees. That was Cold Branch—no boom town, but the slow growth of many years. Cold Branch lay on the edge of the grape and corn lands. The big, country road ran just back of the heights. Cold Branch had nothing in common with the frisky ambition of Okochee with its impertinent lake.

"Mac," said J. Pinkney suddenly, "I want you to stop at Cold Branch. There's a landing there that they made to use sometimes when the river was up."

"Can't," said the captain, grinning more broadly. "I've got the United States mails on board. Right to-day this boat's in the government service. Do you want to have the poor old captain keelhauled by Uncle Sam? And the great city of Skyland, all disconsolate, waiting for its mail? I'm ashamed of your extravagance, J. P."

"Mac," almost whispered J. Pinkney, in his danger-line voice, "I looked into the engine room of the *Dixie Belle* a while ago. Don't you know of somebody that needs a new boiler? Cement and black Japan can't hide flaws from me. And then, those shares of building and loan that you traded for repairs—they were all yours, of course. I hate to mention these things, but——"

"Oh, come now, J. P.," said the captain. "You

know I was just fooling. I'll put you off at Cold Branch, if you say so."

"The other passengers get off there, too," said Mr. Bloom.

Further conversation was held, and in ten minutes the *Dixie Belle* turned her nose toward a little, cranky wooden pier on the left bank, and the captain, relinquishing the wheel to a roustabout, came to the passenger deck and made the remarkable announcement: "All out for Skyland."

The Blaylocks and J. Pinkney Bloom disembarked, and the *Dixie Belle* proceeded on her way up the lake. Guided by the indefatigable promoter, they slowly climbed the steep hillside, pausing often to rest and admire the view. Finally they entered the village of Cold Branch. Warmly both the Colonel and his wife praised it for its homelike and peaceful beauty. Mr. Bloom conducted them to a two-story building on a shady street that bore the legend, "Pine-top Inn." Here he took his leave, receiving the cordial thanks of the two for his attentions, the Colonel remarking that he thought they would spend the remainder of the day in rest, and take a look at his purchase on the morrow.

J. Pinkney Bloom walked down Cold Branch's main street. He did not know this town, but he knew towns, and his feet did not falter. Presently he saw a sign over a door: "Frank E. Cooly, Attorney-at-Law and Notary Public." A young man was Mr. Cooly, and awaiting business.

"Get your hat, son," said Mr. Bloom, in his breezy way, "and a blank deed, and come along. It's a job for you."

"Now," he continued, when Mr. Cooly had responded with alacrity, "is there a bookstore in town?"

"One," said the lawyer. "Henry Williams's."

"Get there," said Mr. Bloom. "We're going to buy it."

Henry Williams was behind his counter. His store was a small one, containing a mixture of books, stationery, and fancy rubbish. Adjoining it was Henry's home—a decent cottage, vine-embowered and cosy. Henry was lank and soporific, and not inclined to rush his business.

"I want to buy your house and store," said Mr. Bloom. "I haven't got time to dicker—name your price."

"It's worth eight hundred," said Henry, too much dazed to ask more than its value.

"Shut that door," said Mr. Bloom to the lawyer. Then he tore off his coat and vest, and began to unbutton his shirt.

"Wanter fight about it, do yer?" said Henry Williams jumping up and cracking his heels together twice. "All right, hunky—sail in and cut yer capers."

"Keep your clothes on," said Mr. Bloom. "I'm only going down to the bank."

He drew eight one-hundred-dollar bills from his money belt and planked them down on the counter.

Mr. Cooly showed signs of future promise, for he already had the deed spread out, and was reaching across the counter for the ink bottle. Never before or since was such quick action had in Cold Branch.

"Your name, please?" asked the lawyer.

"Make it out to Peyton Blaylock," said Mr. Bloom. "God knows how to spell it."

Within thirty minutes Henry Williams was out of business, and Mr. Bloom stood on the brick sidewalk with Mr. Cooly, who held in his hand the signed and attested deed.

"You'll find the party at the Pinetop Inn," said J. Pinkney Bloom. "Get it recorded, and take it down and give it to him. He'll ask you a hell's mint of questions; so here's ten dollars for the trouble you'll have in not being able to answer 'em. Never run much to poetry, did you, young man?"

"Well," said the really talented Cooly, who even yet retained his right mind, "now and then."

"Dig into it," said Mr. Bloom; "it'll pay you. Never heard a poem, now, that run something like this, did you?—

> "A good thing out of Nazareth
>   Comes up sometimes, I guess,
> On hand, all right, to help and cheer
>   A sucker in distress."

"I believe not," said Mr. Cooly.

"It's a hymn," said J. Pinkney Bloom. "Now, show me the way to a livery stable, son, for I'm going to hit the dirt road back to Okochee."

CONFESSIONS OF A HUMOURIST

THERE was a painless stage of incubation that lasted twenty-five years, and then it broke out on me, and people said I was It.

But they called it humour instead of measles.

The employees in the store bought a silver inkstand for the senior partner on his fiftieth birthday. We crowded into his private office to present it.

I had been selected for spokesman, and I made a little speech that I had been preparing for a week.

It made a hit. It was full of puns and epigrams and funny twists that brought down the house—which was a very solid one in the wholesale hardware line. Old Marlowe himself actually grinned, and the employees took their cue and roared.

My reputation as a humourist dates from half-past nine o'clock on that morning.

For weeks afterward my fellow clerks fanned the flame of my self-esteem. One by one they came to me, saying what an awfully clever speech that was, old man, and carefully explained to me the point of each one of my jokes.

Gradually I found that I was expected to keep it up. Others might speak sanely on business matters and the day's topics, but from me something gamesome and airy was required.

I was expected to crack jokes about the crockery and lighten up the granite ware with persiflage. I was second bookkeeper, and if I failed to show up a balance sheet without something comic about the footings or could find no cause for laughter in an invoice of plows, the other clerks were disappointed.

By degrees my fame spread, and I became a local "character." Our town was small enough to make this possible. The daily newspaper quoted me. At social gatherings I was indispensable.

I believe I did possess considerable wit and a facility for quick and spontaneous repartee. This gift I cultivated and improved by practice. And the nature of it was kindly and genial, not running to sarcasm or offending others. People began to smile when they saw me coming, and by the time we had met I generally had the word ready to broaden the smile into a laugh.

I had married early. We had a charming boy of three and a girl of five. Naturally, we lived in a vine-covered cottage, and were happy. My salary as bookkeeper in the hardware concern kept at a distance those ills attendant upon superfluous wealth.

At sundry times I had written out a few jokes and conceits that I considered peculiarly happy, and had sent them to certain periodicals that print such things. All of them had been instantly accepted. Several of the editors had written to request further contributions.

One day I received a letter from the editor of a famous weekly publication. He suggested that I submit to him a humorous composition to fill a column of space; hinting that he would make it a regular feature of each issue if the work proved satisfactory. I did so, and at the end of two weeks he offered to make a contract with me for a year at a figure that was considerably higher than the amount paid me by the hardware firm.

I was filled with delight. My wife already crowned me in her mind with the imperishable evergreens of literary success. We had lobster croquettes and a bottle of blackberry wine for supper that night. Here was the chance to liberate myself from drudgery. I talked over the matter very seriously with Louisa. We agreed that I must resign my place at the store and devote myself to humour.

I resigned. My fellow clerks gave me a farewell banquet. The speech I made there coruscated. It was printed in full by the *Gazette*. The next morning I awoke and looked at the clock.

"Late, by George!" I exclaimed, and grabbed for my clothes. Louisa reminded me that I was no longer a slave to hardware and contractors' supplies. I was now a professional humourist.

After breakfast she proudly led me to the little room off the kitchen. Dear girl! There was my table and chair, writing pad, ink, and pipe tray. And all the author's trappings—the celery stand full of fresh roses and honeysuckle, last year's calendar on the wall, the dictionary, and a little bag of chocolates to nibble between inspirations. Dear girl!

I sat me to work. The wall paper is patterned with arabesques or odalisks or—perhaps—it is trapezoids. Upon one of the figures I fixed my eyes. I bethought me of humour.

A voice startled me—Louisa's voice.

"If you aren't too busy, dear," it said, "come to dinner."

I looked at my watch. Yes, five hours had been gathered in by the grim scytheman. I went to dinner.

"You mustn't work too hard at first," said Louisa. "Goethe—or was it Napoleon?—said five hours a day is enough for mental labour. Couldn't you take me and the children to the woods this afternoon?"

"I *am* a little tired," I admitted. So we went to the woods.

But I soon got the swing of it. Within a month I was turning out copy as regular as shipments of hardware.

And I had success. My column in the weekly made some stir, and I was referred to in a gossipy way by the critics as something fresh in the line of humourists. I augmented my income considerably by contributing to other publications.

I picked up the tricks of the trade. I could take a funny idea and make a two-line joke of it, earning a dollar. With false whiskers on, it would serve up cold as a quatrain, doubling its producing value. By turning the skirt and adding a ruffle of rhyme you would hardly recognize it as *vers de société* with neatly shod feet and a fashion-plate illustration.

I began to save up money, and we had new carpets and a parlour organ. My townspeople began to look upon me as a citizen of some consequence instead of the merry trifler I had been when I clerked in the hardware store.

After five or six months the spontaneity seemed to depart from my humour. Quips and droll sayings no longer fell carelessly from my lips. I was sometimes hard run for material. I found myself listening to catch available ideas from the conversation of my friends. Sometimes I chewed my pencil and gazed at the wall paper for hours trying to build up some gay little bubble of unstudied fun.

And then I became a harpy, a Moloch, a Jonah, a vampire to my acquaintances. Anxious, haggard, greedy, I stood among them like a veritable killjoy. Let a bright saying, a witty comparison, a piquant phrase fall from their lips and I was after it like a hound springing upon a bone. I dared not trust my memory; but, turning aside guiltily and meanly, I would make a note of it in my ever-present memorandum book or upon my cuff for my own future use.

My friends regarded me in sorrow and wonder. I was not the same man. Where once I had furnished them entertainment and jollity, I now preyed upon them. No jests from me ever bid for their smiles now. They were too precious. I could not afford to dispense gratuitously the means of my livelihood.

I was a lugubrious fox praising the singing of my

friends, the crows, that they might drop from their beaks the morsels of wit that I coveted.

Nearly every one began to avoid me. I even forgot how to smile, not even paying that much for the sayings I appropriated.

No persons, places, times, or subjects were exempt from my plundering in search of material. Even in church my demoralized fancy went hunting among the solemn aisles and pillars for spoil.

Did the minister give out the longmeter doxology, at once I began: "Doxology—sockdology—sockdolager—meter—meet her."

The sermon ran through my mental sieve, its precepts filtering unheeded, could I but glean a suggestion of a pun or a *bon mot*. The solemnest anthems of the choir were but an accompaniment to my thoughts as I conceived new changes to ring upon the ancient comicalities concerning the jealousies of soprano, tenor, and basso.

My own home became a hunting ground. My wife is a singularly feminine creature, candid, sympathetic, and impulsive. Once her conversation was my delight, and her ideas a source of unfailing pleasure. Now I worked her. She was a gold mine of those amusing but lovable inconsistencies that distinguish the female mind.

I began to market those pearls of unwisdom and humour that should have enriched only the sacred precincts of home. With devilish cunning I encouraged her to talk. Unsuspecting, she laid her heart bare. Upon the cold, conspicuous, common, printed page I offered it to the public gaze.

A literary Judas, I kissed her and betrayed her. For pieces of silver I dressed her sweet confidences in the pantalettes and frills of folly and made them dance in the market place.

Dear Louisa! Of nights I have bent over her cruel as a wolf above a tender lamb, hearkening even to her soft words murmured in sleep, hoping to catch an idea for my next day's grind. There is worse to come.

God help me! Next my fangs were buried deep in the neck of the fugitive sayings of my little children.

Guy and Viola were two bright fountains of childish, quaint thoughts and speeches. I found a ready sale for this kind of humour, and was furnishing a regular department in a magazine with "Funny Fancies of Childhood." I began to stalk them as an Indian stalks the antelope. I would hide behind sofas and doors, or crawl on my hands and knees among the bushes in the yard to eavesdrop while they were at play. I had all the qualities of a harpy except remorse.

Once, when I was barren of ideas, and my copy must leave in the next mail, I covered myself in a pile of autumn leaves in the yard, where I knew they intended to come to play. I cannot bring myself to believe that Guy was aware of my hiding place, but even if he was, I would be loath to blame him for his setting fire to the leaves, causing the destruction of my new suit of clothes, and nearly cremating a parent.

Soon my own children began to shun me as a pest. Often, when I was creeping upon them like a melancholy ghoul, I would hear them say to each other: "Here comes papa," and they would gather their toys and scurry away to some safer hiding place. Miserable wretch that I was!

And yet I was doing well financially. Before the first year had passed I had saved a thousand dollars, and we had lived in comfort.

But at what a cost! I am not quite clear as to what a pariah is, but I was everything that it sounds like. I had no friends, no amusements, no enjoyment of life. The happiness of my family had been sacrificed. I was a bee, sucking sordid honey from life's fairest flowers, dreaded and shunned on account of my sting.

One day a man spoke to me, with a pleasant and friendly smile. Not in months had the thing happened. I was passing the undertaking establishment of Peter Heffelbower. Peter stood in the door and saluted me. I stopped, strangely wrung in my heart by his greeting. He asked me inside.

The day was chill and rainy. We went into the back room, where a fire burned in a little stove. A customer came, and Peter left me alone for a while. Presently I felt a new feeling stealing over me—a sense of beautiful calm and content. I looked around the place. There were rows of shining rosewood caskets, black palls, trestles, hearse plumes, mourning streamers, and all the paraphernalia of the solemn trade. Here was peace, order, silence, the abode of grave and dignified reflections. Here, on the brink of life, was a little niche pervaded by the spirit of eternal rest.

When I entered it, the follies of the world abandoned me at the door. I felt no inclination to wrest a humorous idea from those sombre and stately trappings. My mind seemed to stretch itself to grateful repose upon a couch draped with gentle thoughts.

A quarter of an hour ago I was an abandoned humourist. Now I was a philosopher, full of serenity and ease. I had found a *refuge* from humour, from the hot chase of the shy quip, from the degrading pursuit of the panting joke, from the restless reach after the nimble repartee.

I had not known Heffelbower well. When he came back, I let him talk, fearful that he might prove to be a jarring note in the sweet, dirgelike harmony of his establishment.

But, no. He chimed truly. I gave a long sigh of happiness. Never have I known a man's talk to be as magnificently dull as Peter's was. Compared with it the Dead Sea is a geyser. Never a sparkle or a glimmer of wit marred his words. Commonplaces as trite and as plentiful as blackberries flowed from his lips no more stirring in quality than a last week's tape running from a ticker. Quaking a little, I tried upon him one of my best pointed jokes. It fell back ineffectual, with the point broken. I loved that man from then on.

Two or three evenings each week I would steal down to Heffelbower's and revel in his back room. That was my only joy. I began to rise early and hurry through my work, that I might spend more time in my haven. In no other place could I throw off my habit of extracting humorous ideas from my surroundings. Peter's talk left me no opening had I besieged it ever so hard.

Under this influence I began to improve in spirits. It was the recreation from one's labour which every man needs. I surprised one or two of my former friends by throwing them a smile and a cheery word as I passed them on the streets. Several times I dumfounded my family by relaxing long enough to make a jocose remark in their presence.

I had so long been ridden by the incubus of humour that I seized my hours of holiday with a schoolboy's zest.

My work began to suffer. It was not the pain and burden to me that it had been. I often whistled at my desk, and wrote with far more fluency than before. I accomplished my tasks impatiently, as anxious to be off to my helpful retreat as a drunkard is to get to his tavern.

My wife had some anxious hours in conjecturing where I spent my afternoons. I thought it best not to tell her; women do not understand these things. Poor girl!—she had one shock out of it.

One day I brought home a silver coffin handle for a paper weight and a fine, fluffy hearse plume to dust my papers with.

I loved to see them on my desk, and think of the beloved back room down at Heffelbower's. But Louisa found them, and she shrieked with horror. I had to console her with some lame excuse for having them, but I saw in her eyes that the prejudice was not removed. I had to remove the articles, though, at double-quick time.

One day Peter Heffelbower laid before me a temptation that swept me off my feet. In his sensible, uninspired way he showed me his books, and explained that his profits and his business were increasing rapidly. He had thought of taking in a partner with some cash. He would rather have me than any one he knew. When I left his place that afternoon Peter had my check for the thousand dollars I had in the bank, and I was a partner in his undertaking business.

I went home with feelings of delirious joy, mingled with a certain amount of doubt. I was dreading to tell my wife about it. But I walked on air. To give up the writing of humorous stuff, once more to enjoy the apples of life, instead of squeezing them to a pulp for a few drops of hard cider to make the public feel funny—what a boon that would be!

At the supper table Louisa handed me some letters that had come during my absence. Several of them contained rejected manuscript. Ever since I first began going to Heffelbower's my stuff had been coming back with alarming frequency. Lately I had been dashing off my jokes and articles with the greatest fluency. Previously I had laboured like a bricklayer, slowly and with agony.

Presently I opened a letter from the editor of the weekly with which I had a regular contract. The checks for that weekly article were still our main dependence. The letter ran thus:

DEAR SIR:

As you are aware, our contract for the year expires with the present month. While regretting the necessity for so doing, we must say that we do not care to renew same for the coming year. We were quite pleased with your style of humour, which seems to have delighted quite a large proportion of our readers. But for the past two months we have noticed a decided falling off in its quality.

Your earlier work showed a spontaneous, easy, natural flow of fun and wit. Of late it is laboured, studied, and unconvincing, giving painful evidence of hard toil and drudging mechanism.

Again regretting that we do not consider your contributions available any longer, we are, yours sincerely,

THE EDITOR.

I handed this letter to my wife. After she had read it her face grew extremely long, and there were tears in her eyes.

"The mean old thing!" she exclaimed indignantly. "I'm sure your pieces are just as good as they ever were. And it doesn't take you half as long to write them as it did." And then, I suppose, Louisa thought of the checks that would cease coming. "Oh, John," she wailed, "what will you do now?"

For an answer I got up and began to do a polka step around the supper table. I am sure Louisa thought the trouble had driven me mad; and I think the children hoped it had, for they tore after me, yelling with glee and emulating my steps. I was now something like their old playmate as of yore.

"The theatre for us to-night!" I shouted; "nothing less. And a late, wild, disreputable supper for all of us at the Palace Restaurant. Lumty-diddle-de-dee-de-dum!"

And then I explained my glee by declaring that I was now a partner in a prosperous undertaking establishment, and that written jokes might go hide their heads in sackcloth and ashes for all me.

With the editor's letter in her hand to justify the deed I had done, my wife could advance no objections save a few mild ones based on the feminine inability to appreciate a good thing such as the little back room of Peter Hef——no, of Heffelbower & Co's. undertaking establishment.

In conclusion, I will say that to-day you will find no man in our town as well liked, as jovial, and full of merry sayings as I. My jokes are again noised about and quoted; once more I take pleasure in my wife's confidential chatter without a mercenary thought, while Guy and Viola play at my feet distributing gems of childish humour without fear of the ghastly tormentor who used to dog their steps, note-book in hand.

Our business has prospered finely. I keep the books and look after the shop, while Peter attends to outside matters. He says that my levity and high spirits would simply turn any funeral into a regular Irish wake.

CONFESSIONS OF A HUMOURIST

THE SPARROWS IN MADISON SQUARE

THE young man in straitened circumstances who comes to New York City to enter literature has but one thing to do, provided he has studied carefully his field in advance. He must go straight to Madison Square, write an article about the sparrows there, and sell it to the *Sun* for $15.

I cannot recall either a novel or a story dealing with the popular theme of the young writer from the provinces who comes to the metropolis to win fame and fortune with his pen in which the hero does not get his start that way. It does seem strange that some author, in casting about for startlingly original plots, has not hit upon the idea of having his hero write about the bluebirds in Union Square and sell it to the *Herald*. But a search through the files of metropolitan fiction counts up overwhelmingly for the sparrows and the old Garden Square, and the *Sun* always writes the check.

Of course it is easy to understand why this first city venture of the budding author is always successful. He is primed by necessity to a superlative effort; mid the iron and stone and marble of the roaring city he has found this spot of singing birds and green grass and trees; every tender sentiment in his nature is battling with the sweet pain of homesick-

66

ness; his genius is aroused as it never may be again; the birds chirp, the tree branches sway, the noise of wheels is forgotten; he writes with his soul in his pen —and he sells it to the *Sun* for $15.

I had read of this custom during many years before I came to New York. When my friends were using their strongest arguments to dissuade me from coming, I only smiled serenely. They did not know of that sparrow graft I had up my sleeve.

When I arrived in New York, and the car took me straight from the ferry up Twenty-third Street to Madison Square, I could hear that $15 check rustling in my inside pocket.

I obtained lodging at an unhyphenated hostelry, and the next morning I was on a bench in Madison Square almost by the time the sparrows were awake. Their melodious chirping, the benignant spring foliage of the noble trees and the clean, fragrant grass reminded me so potently of the old farm I had left that tears almost came into my eyes.

Then, all in a moment, I felt my inspiration. The brave, piercing notes of those cheerful small birds formed a keynote to a wonderful, light, fanciful song of hope and joy and altruism. Like myself, they were creatures with hearts pitched to the tune of woods and fields; as I was, so were they captives by circumstance in the discordant, dull city—yet with how much grace and glee they bore the restraint!

And then the early morning people began to pass through the square to their work—sullen people, with sidelong glances and glum faces, hurrying, hurrying, hurrying. And I got my theme cut out clear from the bird notes, and wrought it into a lesson, and a poem, and a carnival dance, and a lullaby; and then translated it all into prose and began to write.

For two hours my pencil travelled over my pad with scarcely a rest. Then I went to the little room I had rented for two days, and there I cut it to half, and then mailed it, white-hot, to the *Sun.*

The next morning I was up by daylight and spent two cents of my capital for a paper. If the word "sparrow" was in it I was unable to find it.

I took it up to my room and spread it out on the bed and went over it, column by column. Something was wrong.

Three hours afterward the postman brought me a large envelope containing my MS. and a piece of inexpensive paper, about 3 inches by 4—I suppose some of you have seen them—upon which was written in violet ink, "With the *Sun's* thanks."

I went over to the square and sat upon a bench. No; I did not think it necessary to eat any breakfast that morning. The confounded pests of sparrows were making the square hideous with their idiotic "cheep, cheep." I never saw birds so persistently noisy, impudent, and disagreeable in all my life.

By this time, according to all traditions, I should have been standing in the office of the editor of the *Sun.* That personage—a tall, grave, white-haired man—would strike a silver bell as he grasped my hand and wiped a suspicious moisture from his glasses.

"Mr. McChesney," he would be saying when a subordinate appeared, "this is Mr. Henry, the young man who sent in that exquisite gem about the sparrows in Madison Square. You may give him a desk at once. Your salary, sir, will be $80 a week, to begin with."

This was what I had been led to expect by all writers who have evolved romances of literary New York.

Something was decidedly wrong with tradition. I could not assume the blame; so I fixed it upon the sparrows. I began to hate them with intensity and heat.

At that moment an individual wearing an excess of whiskers, two hats, and a pestilential air slid into the seat beside me.

"Say, Willie," he muttered cajolingly, "could you cough up a dime out of your coffers for a cup of coffee this morning?"

"I'm lung-weary, my friend," said I. "The best I can do is three cents."

"And you look like a gentleman, too," said he. "What brung you down—booze?"

"Birds," I said fiercely. "The brown-throated songsters carolling songs of hope and cheer to weary man toiling amid the city's dust and din. The little feathered couriers from the meadows and woods chirping sweetly to us of blue skies and flowering

69

fields. The confounded little squint-eyed nuisances yawping like a flock of steam pianos, and stuffing themselves like aldermen with grass seeds and bugs, while a man sits on a bench and goes without his breakfast. Yes, sir, birds! look at them!"

As I spoke I picked up a dead tree branch that lay by the bench, and hurled it with all my force into a close congregation of the sparrows on the grass. The flock flew to the trees with a babel of shrill cries; but two of them remained prostrate upon the turf.

In a moment my unsavoury friend had leaped over the row of benches and secured the fluttering victims, which he thrust hurriedly into his pockets. Then he beckoned me with a dirty forefinger.

"Come on, cully," he said hoarsely. "You're in on the feed."

Weakly I followed my dingy acquaintance. He led me away from the park down a side street and through a crack in a fence into a vacant lot where some excavating had been going on. Behind a pile of old stones and lumber he paused, and took out his birds.

"I got matches," said he. "You got any paper to start a fire with?"

I drew forth my manuscript story of the sparrows, and offered it for burnt sacrifice. There were old planks, splinters, and chips for our fire. My frowsy friend produced from some interior of his frayed clothing half a loaf of bread, pepper, and salt.

THE SPARROWS IN MADISON SQUARE

In ten minutes each of us was holding a sparrow spitted upon a stick over the leaping flames.

"Say," said my fellow bivouacker, "this ain't so bad when a fellow's hungry. It reminds me of when I struck New York first—about fifteen years ago. I come in from the West to see if I could get a job on a newspaper. I hit the Madison Square Park the first mornin' after, and was sittin' around on the benches. I noticed the sparrows chirpin', and the grass and trees so nice and green that I thought I was back in the country again. Then I got some papers out of my pocket, and——"

"I know," I interrupted. "You sent it to the *Sun* and got $15."

"Say," said my friend, suspiciously, "you seem to know a good deal. Where was you? I went to sleep on the bench there, in the sun, and somebody touched me for every cent I had—$15."

HEARTS AND HANDS

AT DENVER there was an influx of passengers into the coaches on the eastbound B. & M. express. In one coach there sat a very pretty young woman dressed in elegant taste and surrounded by all the luxurious comforts of an experienced traveller. Among the newcomers were two young men, one of handsome presence with a bold, frank countenance and manner; the other a ruffled, glum-faced person, heavily built and roughly dressed. The two were handcuffed together.

As they passed down the aisle of the coach the only vacant seat offered was a reversed one facing the attractive young woman. Here the linked couple seated themselves. The young woman's glance fell upon them with a distant, swift disinterest; then with a lovely smile brightening her countenance and a tender pink tingeing her rounded cheeks, she held out a little gray-gloved hand. When she spoke her voice, full, sweet, and deliberate, proclaimed that its owner was accustomed to speak and be heard.

"Well, Mr. Easton, if you *will* make me speak first, I suppose I must. Don't you ever recognize old friends when you meet them in the West?"

The younger man roused himself sharply at the sound of her voice, seemed to struggle with a slight embarrassment which he threw off instantly, and then clasped her fingers with his left hand.

"It's Miss Fairchild," he said, with a smile. "I'll ask you to excuse the other hand; it's otherwise engaged just at present."

He slightly raised his right hand, bound at the wrist by the shining "bracelet" to the left one of his companion. The glad look in the girl's eyes slowly changed to a bewildered horror. The glow faded from her cheeks. Her lips parted in a vague, relaxing distress. Easton, with a little laugh, as if amused, was about to speak again when the other forestalled him. The glum-faced man had been watching the girl's countenance with veiled glances from his keen, shrewd eyes.

"You'll excuse me for speaking, miss, but I see you're acquainted with the marshal here. If you'll ask him to speak a word for me when we get to the pen he'll do it, and it'll make things easier for me there. He's taking me to Leavenworth prison. It's seven years for counterfeiting."

"Oh!" said the girl, with a deep breath and returning colour. "So, that is what you are doing out here? A marshal!"

"My dear Miss Fairchild," said Easton calmly, "I had to do something. Money has a way of taking wings unto itself, and you know it takes money to keep step with our crowd in Washington. I saw this opening in the West, and—well, a marshalship isn't quite as high a position as that of ambassador, but——"

"The ambassador," said the girl warmly, "doesn't call any more. He needn't ever have done so. You ought to know that. And so now you are one of these dashing Western heroes, and you ride and shoot and go into all kinds of dangers. That's different from the Washington life. You have been missed from the old crowd."

The girl's eyes, fascinated, went back, widening a little, to rest upon the glittering handcuffs.

"Don't you worry about them, miss," said the other man. "All marshals handcuff themselves to their prisoners to keep them from getting away. Mr. Easton knows his business."

"Will we see you again soon in Washington?" asked the girl.

"Not soon, I think," said Easton. "My butterfly days are over, I fear."

"I love the West," said the girl irrelevantly. Her eyes were shining softly. She looked away out the car window. She began to speak truly and simply, without the gloss of style and manner: "Mamma and I spent the summer in Denver. She went home a week ago because father was slightly ill. I could live and be happy in the West. I think the air here agrees with me. Money isn't everything. But people always misunderstand things and remain stupid——"

"Say, Mr. Marshal," growled the glum-faced man. "This isn't quite fair. I'm needin' a drink, and haven't had a smoke all day. Haven't you talked long enough? Take me in the smoker now, won't you? I'm half dead for a pipe."

The bound travellers rose to their feet, Easton with the same slow smile on his face.

"I can't deny a petition for tobacco," he said lightly. "It's the one friend of the unfortunate. Good-bye, Miss Fairchild. Duty calls, you know." He held out his hand for a farewell.

"It's too bad you are not going East," she said, reclothing herself with manner and style. "But you must go on to Leavenworth, I suppose?"

"Yes," said Easton, "I must go on to Leavenworth."

The two men sidled down the aisle into the smoker.

Two passengers in a seat near by had heard most of the conversation. Said one of them: "That marshal's a good sort of chap. Some of these Western fellows are all right."

"Pretty young to hold an office like that, isn't he?" asked the other.

"Young!" exclaimed the first speaker, "why— Oh! didn't you catch on? Say—did you ever know an officer to handcuff a prisoner to his *right* hand?"

THE CACTUS

THE most notable thing about Time is that it is so purely relative. A large amount of reminiscence is, by common consent, conceded to the drowning man; and it is not past belief that one may review an entire courtship while removing one's gloves.

That is what Trysdale was doing, standing by a table in his bachelor apartments. On the table stood a singular-looking green plant in a red earthen jar. The plant was one of the species of cacti, and was provided with long, tentacular leaves that perpetually swayed with the slightest breeze with a peculiar beckoning motion.

Trysdale's friend, the brother of the bride, stood at a sideboard complaining at being allowed to drink alone. Both men were in evening dress. White favours like stars upon their coats shone through the gloom of the apartment.

As he slowly unbuttoned his gloves, there passed through Trysdale's mind a swift, scarifying retrospect of the last few hours. It seemed that in his nostrils was still the scent of the flowers that had been banked in odorous masses about the church, and in his ears the low-pitched hum of a thousand well-bred voices, the rustle of crisp garments, and, most insistently

76

recurring, the drawling words of the minister irrevocably binding her to another.

From this last, hopeless point of view he still strove, as if it had become a habit of his mind, to reach some conjecture as to why and how he had lost her. Shaken rudely by the uncompromising fact, he had suddenly found himself confronted by a thing he had never before faced—his own innermost, unmitigated, and unbedecked self. He saw all the garbs of pretence and egoism that he had worn now turn to rags of folly. He shuddered at the thought that to others, before now, the garments of his soul must have appeared sorry and threadbare. Vanity and conceit! These were the joints in his armour. And how free from either she had always been——But why——

As she had slowly moved up the aisle toward the altar he had felt an unworthy, sullen exultation that had served to support him. He had told himself that her paleness was from thoughts of another than the man to whom she was about to give herself. But even that poor consolation had been wrenched from him. For, when he saw that swift, limpid, upward look that she gave the man when he took her hand, he knew himself to be forgotten. Once that same look had been raised to him, and he had gauged its meaning. Indeed, his conceit had crumbled; its last prop was gone. Why had it ended thus? There had been no quarrel between them, nothing——

For the thousandth time he remarshalled in his

mind the events of those last few days before the
tide had so suddenly turned.

She had always insisted upon placing him upon a
pedestal, and he had accepted her homage with royal
grandeur. It had been a very sweet incense that she
had burned before him; so modest (he told himself),
so childlike and worshipful, and (he would once have
sworn) so sincere. She had invested him with an
almost supernatural number of high attributes and
excellencies and talents, and he had absorbed the
oblation as a desert drinks the rain that can coax
from it no promise of blossom or fruit.

As Trysdale grimly wrenched apart the seam of
his last glove, the crowning instance of his fatuous
and tardily mourned egoism came vividly back to
him.

The scene was the night when he had asked her to
come up on his pedestal with him and share his greatness. He could not, now, for the pain of it, allow his
mind to dwell upon the memory of her convincing
beauty that night—the careless wave of her hair,
the tenderness and virginal charm of her looks and
words. But they had been enough, and they had
brought him to speak. During their conversation
she had said:

"And Captain Carruthers tells me that you speak
the Spanish language like a native. Why have you
hidden this accomplishment from me? Is there anything you do not know?"

Now, Carruthers was an idiot. No doubt he

(Trysdale) had been guilty (he sometimes did such things) of airing at the club some old, canting Castilian proverb dug from the hotch-potch at the back of dictionaries. Carruthers, who was one of his incontinent admirers, was the very man to have magnified this exhibition of doubtful erudition.

But, alas! the incense of her admiration had been so sweet and flattering. He allowed the imputation to pass without denial. Without protest, he allowed her to twine about his brow this spurious bay of Spanish scholarship. He let it grace his conquering head, and, among its soft convolutions, he did not feel the prick of the thorn that was to pierce him later.

How glad, how shy, how tremulous she was! How she fluttered like a snared bird when he laid his mightiness at her feet! He could have sworn, and he could swear now, that unmistakable consent was in her eyes, but, coyly, she would give him no direct answer. "I will send you my answer to-morrow," she said; and he, the indulgent, confident victor, smilingly granted the delay.

The next day he waited, impatient, in his rooms for the word. At noon her groom came to the door and left the strange cactus in the red earthen jar. There was no note, no message, merely a tag upon the plant bearing a barbarous foreign or botanical name. He waited until night, but her answer did not come. His large pride and hurt vanity kept him from seeking her. Two evenings later they met at a dinner. Their greetings were conventional, but she looked at him, breathless, wondering, eager. He was courteous, adamant, waiting her explanation. With womanly swiftness she took her cue from his manner, and turned to snow and ice. Thus, and wider from this on, they had drifted apart. Where was his fault? Who had been to blame? Humbled now, he sought the answer amid the ruins of his self-conceit. If——

The voice of the other man in the room, querulously intruding upon his thoughts, aroused him.

"I say, Trysdale, what the deuce is the matter with you? You look unhappy as if you yourself had been married instead of having acted merely as an accomplice. Look at me, another accessory, come two thousand miles on a garlicky, cockroachy banana steamer all the way from South America to connive at the sacrifice—please to observe how lightly my guilt rests upon my shoulders. Only little sister I had, too, and now she's gone. Come now! take something to ease your conscience."

"I won't drink just now, thanks," said Trysdale.

"Your brandy," resumed the other, coming over and joining him, "is abominable. Run down to see me some time at Punta Redonda, and try some of our stuff that old Garcia smuggles in. It's worth the trip. Hallo! here's an old acquaintance. Wherever did you rake up this cactus, Trysdale?"

"A present," said Trysdale, "from a friend. Know the species?"

"Very well. It's a tropical concern. See hundreds of 'em around Punta every day. Here's the name on this tag tied to it. Know any Spanish, Trysdale?"

"No," said Trysdale, with the bitter wraith of a smile—"Is it Spanish?"

"Yes. The natives imagine the leaves are reaching out and beckoning to you. They call it by this name—*Ventomarme*. Name means in English, 'Come and take me.'"

THE DETECTIVE DETECTOR

I WAS walking in Central Park with Avery Knight the great New York burglar, highwayman, and murderer.

"But, my dear Knight," said I, "it sounds incredible. You have undoubtedly performed some of the most wonderful feats in your profession known to modern crime. You have committed some marvellous deeds under the very noses of the police—you have boldly entered the homes of millionaries and held them up with an empty gun while you made free with their silver and jewels; you have sandbagged citizens in the glare of Broadway's electric lights; you have killed and robbed with superb openness and absolute impunity—but when you boast that within forty-eight hours after committing a murder you can run down and actually bring me face to face with the detective assigned to apprehend you, I must beg leave to express my doubts—remember, you are in New York."

Avery Knight smiled indulgently.

"You pique my professional pride, doctor," he said in a nettled tone. "I will convince you."

About twelve yards in advance of us a prosperous-looking citizen was rounding a clump of bushes where the walk curved. Knight suddenly drew a revolver and shot the man in the back. His victim fell and lay without moving.

The great murderer went up to him leisurely and took from his clothes his money, watch, and a valuable ring and cravat pin. He then rejoined me smiling calmly, and we continued our walk.

Ten steps and we met a policeman running toward the spot where the shot had been fired. Avery Knight stopped him.

"I have just killed a man," he announced, seriously, "and robbed him of his possessions."

"G'wan," said the policeman, angrily, "or I'll run yez in! Want yer name in the papers, don't yez? I never knew the cranks to come around so quick after a shootin' before. Out of th' park, now, for yours, or I'll fan yez."

"What you have done," I said argumentatively, as Knight and I walked on, "was easy. But when you come to the task of hunting down the detective that they send upon your trail you will find that you have undertaken a difficult feat."

"Perhaps so," said Knight lightly. "I will admit that my success depends in a degree upon the sort of man they start after me. If it should be an ordinary plain-clothes man I might fail to gain a sight of him. If they honour me by giving the case to some one of their celebrated sleuths I do not fear to match my cunning and powers of induction against his."

On the next afternoon Knight entered my office with a satisfied look on his keen countenance.

"How goes the mysterious murder?" I asked.

"As usual," said Knight smilingly. "I have put in the morning at the police station and at the inquest. It seems that a card case of mine containing cards with my name and address was found near the body. They have three witnesses who saw the shooting and gave a description of me. The case has been placed in the hands of Shamrock Jolnes, the famous detective. He left Headquarters at 11:30 on the assignment. I waited at my address until two, thinking he might call there."

I laughed tauntingly.

"You will never see Jolnes," I continued, "until this murder has been forgotten, two or three weeks from now. I had a better opinion of your shrewdness, Knight. During the three hours and a half that you waited he has got out of your ken. He is after you on true induction theories now, and no wrongdoer has yet been known to come upon him while thus engaged. I advise you to give it up."

"Doctor," said Knight, with a sudden glint in his keen gray eye and a squaring of his chin, "in spite of the record your city holds of something like a dozen homicides without a subsequent meeting of the perpetrator and the sleuth in charge of the case, I will undertake to break that record. To-morrow I will take you to Shamrock Jolnes—I will unmask him before you and prove to you that it is not an impossibility for an officer of the law and a man-slayer to stand face to face in your city."

"Do it," said I, "and you'll have the sincere thanks of the Police Department."

On the next day Knight called for me in a cab.

"I've been on one or two false scents, doctor," he admitted. "I know something of detectives' methods, and I followed out a few of them, expecting to find Jolnes at the other end. The pistol being a .45-calibre, I thought surely I would find him at work on the clue in Forty-fifth Street. Then, again, I looked for the detective at the Columbia University, as the man's being shot in the back naturally suggested hazing. But I could not find a trace of him."

"Nor will you," I said emphatically.

"Not by ordinary methods," said Knight. "I might walk up and down Broadway for a month without success. But you have aroused my pride, doctor; and if I fail to show you Shamrock Jolnes this day, I promise you I will never kill or rob in your city again."

"Nonsense, man," I replied. "When our burglars walk into our houses and politely demand thousands of dollars' worth of jewels, and then dine and bang the piano an hour or two before leaving, how do you, a mere murderer, expect to come in contact with the detective that is looking for you?"

Avery Knight sat lost in thought for a while. At length he looked up brightly.

"Doc," said he, "I have it. Put on your hat, and come with me. In half an hour I guarantee that you shall stand in the presence of Shamrock Jolnes."

I entered a cab with Avery Knight. I did not hear his instructions to the driver, but the vehicle set out at a smart pace up Broadway, turning presently into Fifth Avenue, and proceeding northward again. It was with a rapidly beating heart that I accompanied this wonderful and gifted assassin, whose analytical genius and superb self-confidence had prompted him to make me the tremendous promise of bringing me into the presence of a murderer and the New York detective in pursuit of him simultaneously. Even yet I could not believe it possible.

"Are you sure that you are not being led into some trap?" I asked. "Suppose that your clue, whatever it is, should bring us only into the presence of the Commissioner of Police and a couple of dozen cops!"

"My dear doctor," said Knight, a little stiffly. "I would remind you that I am no gambler."

"I beg your pardon," said I. "But I do not think you will find Jolnes."

The cab stopped before one of the handsomest residences on the avenue. Walking up and down in front of the house was a man with long red whiskers, with a detective's badge showing on the lapel of his coat. Now and then the man would remove his whiskers to wipe his face, and then I would recognize at once the well-known features of the great New York detective. Jolnes was keeping a sharp watch upon the doors and windows of the house.

"Well, doctor," said Knight, unable to repress a note of triumph in his voice, "have you seen?"

"It is wonderful—wonderful!" I could not help exclaiming, as our cab started on its return trip. "But how did you do it? By what process of induction——"

"My dear doctor," interrupted the great murderer, "the inductive theory is what the detectives use. My process is more modern. I call it the saltatorial theory. Without bothering with the tedious mental phenomena necessary to the solution of a mystery from slight clues, I jump at once to a conclusion. I will explain to you the method I employed in this case.

"In the first place, I argued that as the crime was committed in New York City in broad daylight, in a public place and under peculiarly atrocious circumstances, and that as the most skilful sleuth available was let loose upon the case, the perpetrator would never be discovered. Do you not think my postulation justified by precedent?"

"Perhaps so," I replied doggedly. "But if Big Bill Dev——"

"Stop that," interrupted Knight, with a smile. "I've heard that several times. It's too late now. I will proceed.

"If homicides in New York went undiscovered, I reasoned, although the best detective talent was employed to ferret them out, it must be true that the detectives went about their work in the wrong way.

And not only in the wrong way, but exactly opposite
from the right way. That was my clue.

"I slew the man in Central Park. Now, let me
describe myself to you.

"I am tall, with a black beard, and I hate publicity. I have no money to speak of; I do not like
oatmeal, and it is the one ambition of my life to die
rich. I am of a cold and heartless disposition. I do
not care for my fellow-men and I never give a cent
to beggars or charity.

"Now, my dear doctor, that is the true description
of myself, the man whom that shrewd detective was
to hunt down. You who are familiar with the history of crime in New York of late should be able to
foretell the result. When I promised you to ex-
hibit to your incredulous gaze the sleuth who was
set upon me, you laughed at me because you said
that detectives and murderers never met in New
York. I have demonstrated to you that the theory
is possible."

"But how did you do it?" I asked again.

"It was very simple," replied the distinguished
murderer. "I assumed that the detective would go
exactly opposite to the clues he had. I have given
you a description of myself. Therefore, he must nec-
essarily set to work and trail a short man with a
white beard who likes to be in the papers, who is
very wealthy, is fond of oatmeal, wants to die poor,
and is of an extremely generous and philanthropic
disposition. When thus far is reached the mind

hesitates no longer. I conveyed you at once to the spot where Shamrock Jolnes was piping off Andrew Carnegie's residence."

"Knight," said I, "you're a wonder. If there was no danger of your reforming, what a roundsman you'd make for the Nineteenth Precinct!"

THE DOG AND THE PLAYLET*

USUALLY it is a cold day in July when you can stroll up Broadway in that month and get a story out of the drama. I found one a few breathless, parboiling days ago, and it seems to decide a serious question in art.

There was not a soul left in the city except Hollis and I—and two or three million sun-worshippers who remained at desks and counters. The elect had fled to seashore, lake, and mountain, and had already begun to draw for additional funds. Every evening Hollis and I prowled about the deserted town searching for coolness in empty cafés, dining-rooms, and roof-gardens. We knew to the tenth part of a revolution the speed of every electric fan in Gotham, and we followed the swiftest as they varied. Hollis's fiancée, Miss Loris Sherman, had been in the Adirondacks, at Lower Saranac Lake, for a month. In another week he would join her party there. In the meantime, he cursed the city cheerfully and optimistically, and sought my society because I suffered him to show me her photograph during the black coffee every time we dined together.

* This story has been rewritten and published in "Strictly Business" under the title, The Proof of the Pudding.

90

THE DOG AND THE PLAYLET

My revenge was to read to him my one-act play.

It was one insufferable evening when the overplus of the day's heat was being hurled quiveringly back to the heavens by every surcharged brick and stone and inch of iron in the panting town. But with the cunning of the two-legged beasts we had found an oasis where the hoofs of Apollo's steed had not been allowed to strike. Our seats were on an ocean of cool, polished oak; the white linen of fifty deserted tables flapped like seagulls in the artificial breeze; a mile away a waiter lingered for a heliographic signal—we might have roared songs there or fought a duel without molestation.

Out came Miss Loris's photo with the coffee, and I once more praised the elegant poise of the neck, the extremely low-coiled mass of heavy hair, and the eyes that followed one, like those in an oil painting.

"She's the greatest ever," said Hollis, with enthusiasm. "Good as Great Northern preferred, and a disposition built like a watch. One week more and I'll be happy Johnny-on-the-spot. Old Tom Tolliver, my best college chum, went up there two weeks ago. He writes me that Loris doesn't talk about anything but me. Oh, I guess Rip Van Winkle didn't have all the good luck!"

"Yes, yes," said I, hurriedly, pulling out my typewritten play. "She's no doubt a charming girl. Now, here's that little curtain-raiser you promised to listen to."

"Ever been tried on the stage?" asked Hollis.

"Not exactly," I answered. "I read half of it the other day to a fellow whose brother knows Robert Edeson; but he had to catch a train before I finished."

"Go on," said Hollis, sliding back in his chair like a good fellow. "I'm no stage carpenter, but I'll tell you what I think of it from a first row balcony standpoint. I'm a theatre bug during the season, and I can size up a fake play almost as quick as the gallery can. Flag the waiter once more, and then go ahead as hard as you like with it. I'll be the dog."

I read my little play lovingly, and, I fear, not without some elocution. There was one scene in it that I believed in greatly. The comedy swiftly rises into thrilling and unexpectedly developed drama. Capt. Marchmont suddenly becomes cognizant that his wife is an unscrupulous adventuress, who has deceived him from the day of their first meeting. The rapid and mortal duel between them from that moment—she with her magnificent lies and siren charm, winding about him like a serpent, trying to recover her lost ground; he with his man's agony and scorn and lost faith, trying to tear her from his heart. That scene I always thought was a crackerjack. When Capt. Marchmont discovers her duplicity by reading on a blotter in a mirror the impression of a note that she has written to the Count, he raises his hand to heaven and exclaims: "O God, who created woman while Adam slept,

and gave her to him for a companion, take back
thy gift and return instead the sleep, though it last
forever!"

"Rot!" said Hollis, rudely, when I had given those
lines with proper emphasis.

"I beg your pardon!" I said as sweetly as I could.

"Come now," went on Hollis, "don't be an idiot.
You know very well that nobody spouts any stuff
like that these days. That sketch went along all
right until you rang in the skyrockets. Cut out
that right-arm exercise and the Adam and Eve
stunt, and make your captain talk as you or I or
Bill Jones would."

"I'll admit," said I, earnestly (for my theory was
being touched upon), "that on all ordinary occasions
all of us use commonplace language to convey our
thoughts. You will remember that up to the moment when the captain makes his terrible discovery
all the characters on the stage talk pretty much as
they would in real life. But I believe that I am
right in allowing him lines suitable to the strong
and tragic situation into which he falls."

"Tragic, my eye!" said my friend irreverently.
"In Shakespeare's day he might have sputtered out
some high-cockalorum nonsense of that sort, because in those days they ordered ham and eggs in
blank verse and discharged the cook with an epic.
But not for B'way in the summer of 1905!"

"It is my opinion," said I, "that great human
emotions shake up our vocabulary and leave the

words best suited to express them on top. A sudden violent grief or loss or disappointment will bring expressions out of an ordinary man as strong and solemn and dramatic as those used in fiction or on the stage to portray those emotions."

"That's where you fellows are wrong," said Hollis. "Plain, every-day talk is what goes. Your captain would very likely have kicked the cat, lit a cigar, stirred up a highball, and telephoned for a lawyer, instead of getting off those Robert Mantell pyro-technics."

"Possibly, a little later," I continued. "But just at the time—just as the blow is delivered, if some-thing Scriptural or theatrical and deep-tongued isn't wrung from a man in spite of his modern and practical way of speaking, then I'm wrong."

"Of course," said Hollis, kindly, "you've got to whoop her up some degrees for the stage. The audience expects it. When the villain kidnaps little Effie you have to make her mother claw some chunks out of the atmosphere, and scream: 'Me chee-ild, me chee-ild!' What she would actually do would be to call up the police by 'phone, ring for some strong tea, and get the little darling's photo out, ready for the reporters. When you get your villain in a corner —a stage corner—it's all right for him to clap his hand to his forehead and hiss: 'All is lost!' Off the stage he would remark: 'This is a conspiracy against me—I refer you to my lawyers.'"

"I get no consolation," said I, gloomily, "from

your concession of an accentuated stage treatment. In my play I fondly hoped that I was following life. If people in real life meet great crises in a commonplace way, they should do the same on the stage."

And then we drifted, like two trout, out of our cool pool in the great hotel and began to nibble languidly at the gay flies in the swift current of Broadway. And our question of dramatic art was unsettled.

We nibbled at the flies, and avoided the hooks, as wise trout do; but soon the weariness of Manhattan in summer overcame us. Nine stories up, facing the south, was Hollis's apartment, and we soon stepped into an elevator bound for that cooler haven.

I was familiar in those quarters, and quickly my play was forgotten, and I stood at a sideboard mixing things, with cracked ice and glasses all about me. A breeze from the bay came in the windows not altogether blighted by the asphalt furnace over which it had passed. Hollis, whistling softly, turned over a late-arrived letter or two on his table, and drew around the coolest wicker arm-chairs.

I was just measuring the Vermouth carefully when I heard a sound. Some man's voice groaned hoarsely: "False, oh, God!—false, and Love is a lie and friendship but the byword of devils!"

I looked around quickly. Hollis lay across the table with his head down upon his outstretched arms. And then he looked up at me and laughed in his ordinary manner.

I knew him—he was poking fun at me about my theory. And it did seem so unnatural, those swelling words during our quiet gossip, that I half began to believe I had been mistaken—that my theory was wrong.

Hollis raised himself slowly from the table.

"You were right about that theatrical business, old man," he said, quietly, as he tossed a note to me.

I read it.

Loris had run away with Tom Tolliver.

A LITTLE TALK ABOUT MOBS

I SEE," remarked the tall gentleman in the frock coat and black slouch hat, "that another street car motorman in your city has narrowly escaped lynching at the hands of an infuriated mob by lighting a cigar and walking a couple of blocks down the street."

"Do you think they would have lynched him?" asked the New Yorker, in the next seat of the ferry station, who was also waiting for the boat.

"Not until after the election," said the tall man, cutting a corner off his plug of tobacco. "I've been in your city long enough to know something about your mobs. The motorman's mob is about the least dangerous of them all, except the National Guard and the Dressmakers' Convention.

"You see, when little Willie Goldstein is sent by his mother for pigs' knuckles, with a nickel tightly grasped in his chubby fist, he always crosses the street car track safely twenty feet ahead of the car; and then suddenly turns back to ask his mother whether it was pale ale or a spool of 80 white cotton that she wanted. The motorman yells and throws himself on the brakes like a football player. There is a horrible grinding, and then a ripping sound, and a piercing shriek, and Willie is sitting, with part of his trousers

97

torn away by the fender, screaming for his lost nickel.

"In ten seconds the car is surrounded by 600 infuriated citizens, crying, 'Lynch the motorman! Lynch the motorman!' at the top of their voices. Some of them run to the nearest cigar store to get a rope; but they find the last one has just been cut up and labelled. Hundreds of the excited mob press close to the cowering motorman, whose hand is observed to tremble perceptibly as he transfers a stick of pepsin gum from his pocket to his mouth.

"When the bloodthirsty mob of maddened citizens has closed in on the motorman, some bringing camp stools and sitting quite close to him, and all shouting, 'Lynch him!' Policeman Fogarty forces his way through them to the side of their prospective victim.

"'Hello, Mike,' says the motorman in a low voice, 'nice day. Shall I sneak off a block or so, or would you like to rescue me?'

"'Well, Jerry, if you don't mind,' says the policeman, 'I'd like to disperse the infuriated mob singlehanded. I haven't defeated a lynching mob since last Tuesday; and that was a small one of only 300, that wanted to string up a Dago boy for selling wormy pears. It would boost me some down at the station.'

"'All right, Mike,' says the motorman, 'anything to oblige. I'll turn pale and tremble.'

"And he does so; and Policeman Fogarty draws his club and says, 'G'wan wid yez!' and in eight seconds the desperate mob has scattered and gone about its business, except about a hundred who remain to search for Willie's nickel."

"I never heard of a mob in our city doing violence to a motorman because of an accident," said the New Yorker.

"You are not liable to," said the tall man. "They know the motorman's all right, and that he wouldn't even run over a stray dog if he could help it. And they know that not a man among 'em would tie the knot to hang even a Thomas cat that had been tried and condemned and sentenced according to law."

"Then why do they become infuriated and make threats of lynching?" asked the New Yorker.

"To assure the motorman," answered the tall man, "that he is safe. If they really wanted to do him up they would go into the houses and drop bricks on him from the third-story windows."

"New Yorkers are not cowards," said the other man, a little stiffly.

"Not one at a time," agreed the tall man promptly. "You've got a fine lot of single-handed scrappers in your town. I'd rather fight three of you than one; and I'd go up against all the Gas Trust's victims in a bunch before I'd pass two citizens on a dark corner, with my watch chain showing. When you get rounded up in a bunch you lose your nerve. Get you in crowds and you're easy. Ask the 'L' road guards and George B. Cortelyou and the tintype booths at Coney Island. Divided you stand, united you fall.

E pluribus nihil. Whenever one of your mobs surrounds a man and begins to holler, 'Lynch him!' he says to himself, 'Oh, dear, I suppose I must look pale to please the boys, but I will, forsooth, let my life insurance premium lapse to-morrow. This is a sure tip for me to play Methuselah straight across the board in the next handicap.'

"I can imagine the tortured feelings of a prisoner in the hands of New York policemen when an infuriated mob demands that he be turned over to them for lynching. 'For God's sake, officers,' cries the distracted wretch, 'have ye hearts of stone, that ye will not let them wrest me from ye?'

"'Sorry, Jimmy,' says one of the policemen, 'but it won't do. There's three of us—me and Darrell and the plain-clothes man; and there's only sivin thousand of the mob. How'd we explain it at the office if they took ye? Jist chase the infuriated aggregation around the corner, Darrell, and we'll be movin' along to the station.'"

"Some of our gatherings of excited citizens have not been so harmless," said the New Yorker, with a faint note of civic pride.

"I'll admit that," said the tall man. "A cousin of mine who was on a visit here once had an arm broken and lost an ear in one of them."

"That must have been during the Cooper Union riots," remarked the New Yorker.

"Not the Cooper Union," explained the tall man— "but it was a union riot—at the Vanastor wedding."

"You seem to be in favour of lynch law," said the New Yorker severely.

"No, sir, I am not. No intelligent man is. But, sir, there are certain cases when the people rise in their just majesty and take a righteous vengeance for crimes that the law is slow in punishing. I am an advocate of law and order, but I will say to you that less than six months ago I myself assisted at the lynching of one of that race that is creating a wide chasm between your section of country and mine, sir."

"It is a deplorable condition," said the New Yorker, "that exists in the South, but——"

"I am from Indiana, sir," said the tall man, taking another chew; "and I don't think you will condemn my course when I tell you that the coloured man in question had stolen $9.60 cents in cash, sir, from my own brother."

THE SNOW MAN

EDITORIAL NOTE.—*Before the fatal illness of William Sydney Porter (known through his literary work as "O. Henry") this American master of short-story writing had begun for Hampton's Magazine the story printed below. Illness crept upon him rapidly and he was compelled to give up writing about at the point where the girl enters the story.*

When he realized that he could do no more (it was his life-long habit to write with a pencil, never dictating to a stenographer), O. Henry told in detail the remainder of The Snow Man to Harris Merton Lyon, whom he had often spoken of as one of the most effective short-story writers of the present time. Mr. Porter had delineated all of the characters, leaving only the rounding out of the plot in the final pages to Mr. Lyon.

HOUSED and windowpaned from it, the greatest wonder to little children is the snow. To men, it is something like a crucible in which their world melts into a white star ten million miles away. The man who can stand the test is a Snow Man; and this is his reading by Fahrenheit, Réaumur, or Moses' carven tables of stone.

Night had fluttered a sable pinion above the cañon of Big Lost River, and I urged my horse toward the Bay Horse Ranch because the snow was deepening. The flakes were as large as an hour's circular tatting by Miss Wilkins' ablest spinster, betokening a heavy snowfall and less entertainment and more adventure than the completion of the tatting could promise. I knew Ross Curtis of the Bay Horse, and that I would be welcome as a snow-bound pilgrim, both for hospitality's sake and because Ross had few chances to confide in living creatures who did not neigh, bellow, bleat, yelp, or howl, during his discourse.

The ranch house was just within the jaws of the cañon where its builder may have fatuously fancied that the timbered and rocky walls on both sides would have protected it from the wintry Colorado winds; but I feared the drift. Even now through the endless, bottomless rift in the hills—the speaking tube of the four winds—came roaring the voice of the proprietor to the little room on the top floor.

At my "hello," a ranch hand came from an outer building and received my thankful horse. In another minute, Ross and I sat by a stove in the dining-room of the four-room ranch house, while the big, simple welcome of the household lay at my disposal. Fanned by the whizzing norther, the fine, dry snow was sifted and bolted through the cracks and knot-holes of the logs. The cook room, without a separating door, appended.

In there I could see a short, sturdy, leisurely, and weather-beaten man moving with professional sureness about his red-hot stove. His face was stolid and unreadable—something like that of a great thinker, or of one who had no thoughts to conceal. I thought his eye seemed unwarrantably superior to the elements and to the man, but quickly attributed that to the characteristic self-importance of a petty chef. "Camp cook" was the niche that I gave him in the Hall of Types; and he fitted it as an apple fits a dumpling.

Cold it was in spite of the glowing stove; and Ross and I sat and talked, shuddering frequently, half from nerves and half from the freezing draughts. So he brought the bottle, and the cook brought boiling water, and we made prodigious hot toddies against the attacks of Boreas. We clinked glasses often. They sounded like icicles dropping from the eaves, or like the tinkle of a thousand prisms on a Louis XIV chandelier that I once heard at a boarders' dance in the parlour of a ten-a-week boarding-house in Gramercy Square. *Sic transit.*

Silence in the terrible beauty of the snow and of the Sphinx and of the stars; but they who believe that all things, from a without-wine table d'hôte to the crucifixion, may be interpreted through music, might have found a nocturne or a symphony to express the isolation of that blotted-out world. The clink of glass and bottle, the aeolian chorus of the wind in the house crannies, its deeper trombone through the cañon below, and the Wagnerian crash of the cook's pots and pans, united in a fit, discordant melody, I thought. No less welcome an accompaniment was the sizzling of broiling ham and venison cutlets, indorsed by the solvent fumes of true Java, bringing rich promises of comfort to our yearning souls.

The cook brought the smoking supper to the table. He nodded to me democratically as he cast the heavy plates around as though he were pitching quoits or hurling the discus. I looked at him with some appraisement and curiosity, and much conciliation. There was no prophet to tell us when that drifting evil outside might cease to fall; and it is well, when snow-bound, to stand somewhere within the radius of the cook's favourable consideration. But I could read neither favour nor disapproval in the face and manner of our pot-wrestler.

He was about five feet nine inches, and two hundred pounds of commonplace, bull-necked, pink-faced, callous calm. He wore brown duck trousers too tight and too short, and a blue flannel shirt with sleeves rolled above his elbows. There was a sort of grim, steady scowl on his features that looked to me as though he had fixed it there purposely as a protection against the weakness of an inherent amiability that, he fancied, were better concealed. And then I let supper usurp his brief occupancy of my thoughts.

"Draw up, George," said Ross. "Let's all eat while the grub's hot."

"You fellows go on and chew," answered the cook. "I ate mine in the kitchen before sundown."

"Think it'll be a big snow, George?" asked the ranchman.

George had turned to reënter the cook room. He moved slowly around and, looking at his face, it seemed to me that he was turning over the wisdom and knowledge of centuries in his head.

"It might," was his delayed reply.

At the door of the kitchen he stopped and looked

back at us. Both Ross and I held our knives and forks poised and gave him our regard. Some men have the power of drawing the attention of others without speaking a word. Their attitude is more effective than a shout.

"And again it mightn't," said George, and went back to his stove.

After we had eaten, he came in and gathered the emptied dishes. He stood for a moment, with his spurious frown deepened.

"It might stop any minute," he said, "or it might keep it up for days."

At the farther end of the cook room I saw George pour hot water into his dishpan, light his pipe, and put the tableware through its required lavation. He then carefully unwrapped from a piece of old saddle blanket a paper-back book, and settled himself to read by his dim oil lamp.

And then the ranchman threw tobacco on the cleared table and set forth again the bottles and glasses; and I saw that I stood in a deep channel through which the long dammed flood of his discourse would soon be booming. But I was half content, comparing my fate with that of the late Thomas Tucker, who had to sing for his supper, thus doubling the burdens of both himself and his host.

"Snow is a hell of a thing," said Ross, by way of a foreword. "It ain't, somehow, it seems to me, salubrious. I can stand water and mud and two inches below zero and a hundred and ten in the shade and medium-sized cyclones, but this here fuzzy white stuff naturally gets me all locoed. I reckon the reason it rattles you is because it changes the look of things so much. It's like you had a wife and left her in the morning with the same old blue cotton wrapper on, and rides in of a night and runs across her all outfitted in a white silk evening frock, waving an ostrich-feather fan, and monkeying with a posy of lily flowers. Wouldn't it make you look for your pocket compass? You'd be liable to kiss her before you collected your presence of mind."

By and by, the flood of Ross's talk was drawn up into the clouds (so it pleased me to fancy) and there condensed into the finer snowflakes of thought; and we sat silent about the stove, as good friends and bitter enemies will do. I thought of Ross's preamble about the mysterious influence upon man exerted by that ermine-lined monster that now covered our little world, and knew he was right.

Of all the curious knickknacks, mysteries, puzzles, Indian gifts, rat-traps, and well-disguised blessings that the gods chuck down to us from the Olympian peaks, the most disquieting and evil-bringing is the snow. By scientific analysis it is absolute beauty and purity—so, at the beginning we look doubtfully at chemistry.

It falls upon the world, and lo! we live in another. It hides in a night the old scars and familiar places with which we have grown heartsick or enamoured. So, as quietly as we can, we hustle on our embroidered

robes and hie us on Prince Camaralzaman's horse or
in the reindeer sleigh into the white country where
the seven colours converge. This is when our fancy
can overcome the bane of it.

But in certain spots of the earth comes the snow-
madness, made known by people turned wild and
distracted by the bewildering veil that has obscured
the only world they know. In the cities, the white
fairy who sets the brains of her dupes whirling by a
wave of her wand is cast for the comedy rôle. Her
diamond shoe buckles glitter like frost; with a pirou-
ette she invites the spotless carnival.

But in the waste places the snow is sardonic.
Sponging out the world of the outliers, it gives no
foothold on another sphere in return. It makes of the
earth a firmament under foot; it leaves us clawing and
stumbling in space in an inimical fifth element whose
evil outdoes its strangeness and beauty. There
Nature, low comedienne, plays her tricks on man.
Though she has put him forth as her highest product,
it appears that she has fashioned him with what seems
almost incredible carelessness and indexterity. One-
sided and without balance, with his two halves un-
equally fashioned and joined, must he ever jog his
eccentric way. The snow falls, the darkness caps it,
and the ridiculous man-biped strays in accurate
circles until he succumbs in the ruins of his defective
architecture.

In the throat of the thirsty the snow is vitriol. In
appearance as plausible as the breakfast food of the

angels, it is as hot in the mouth as ginger, increasing the pangs of the water-famished. It is a derivative from water, air, and some cold, uncanny fire from which the caloric has been extracted. Good has been said of it; even the poets, crazed by its spell and shivering in their attics under its touch, have indited permanent melodies commemorative of its beauty.

Still, to the saddest overcoated optimist it is a plague—a corroding plague that Pharaoh successfully sidestepped. It beneficently covers the wheat fields, swelling the crop—and the Flour Trust gets us by the throat like a sudden quinsy. It spreads the tail of its white kirtle over the red seams of the rugged north—and the Alaskan short story is born. Etiolated perfidy, it shelters the mountain traveller burrowing from the icy air—and, melting to-morrow, drowns his brother in the valley below.

At its worst it is lock and key and crucible, and the wand of Circe. When it corrals man in lonely ranches, mountain cabins, and forest huts, the snow makes apes and tigers of the hardiest. It turns the bosoms of weaker ones to glass, their tongues to infants' rattles, their hearts to lawlessness and spleen. It is not all from the isolation; the snow is not merely a blockader; it is a Chemical Test. It is a good man who can show a reaction that is not chiefly composed of a drachm or two of potash and magnesia, with traces of Adam, Ananias, Nebuchadnezzar, and the fretful porcupine.

This is no story, you say; well, let it begin.

There was a knock at the door (is the opening not full of context and reminiscence oh, best buyers of best sellers?).

We drew the latch, and in stumbled Étienne Girod (as he afterward named himself). But just then he was no more than a worm struggling for life, enveloped in a killing white chrysalis.

We dug down through snow, overcoats, mufflers, and waterproofs, and dragged forth a living thing with a Van Dyck beard and marvellous diamond rings. We put it through the approved curriculum of snow-rubbing, hot milk, and teaspoonful doses of whisky, working him up to a graduating class entitled to a diploma of three fingers of rye in half a glassful of hot water. One of the ranch boys had already come from the quarters at Ross's bugle-like yell and kicked the stranger's staggering pony to some sheltered corral where beasts were entertained.

Let a paragraphic biography of Girod intervene.

Étienne was an opera singer originally, we gathered; but adversity and the snow had made him *non compos vocis*. The adversity consisted of the stranded San Salvador Opera Company, a period of hotel second-story work, and then a career as a professional palmist, jumping from town to town. For, like other professional palmists, every time he worked the Heart Line too strongly he immediately moved along the Line of Least Resistance. Though Étienne did not confide this to us, we surmised he had moved out into the dusk about twenty minutes ahead of a constable, and had thus encountered the snow. In his most sacred blue language he dilated upon the subject of snow; for Étienne was Paris-born and loved the snow with the same passion that an orchid does.

"Mee-ser-rhable!" commented Étienne, and took another three fingers.

"Complete, cast-iron, pussy-footed, blank . . . blank!" said Ross, and followed suit.

"Rotten," said I.

The cook said nothing. He stood in the door, weighing our outburst; and insistently from behind that frozen visage I got two messages (*via* the M. A. M. wireless). One was that George considered our vituperation against the snow childish; the other was that George did not love Dagoes. Inasmuch as Étienne was a Frenchman, I concluded I had the message wrong. So I queried the other: "Bright eyes, you don't really mean Dagoes, do you?" and over the wireless came three deathly, psychic taps: "Yes." Then I reflected that to George all foreigners were probably "Dagoes." I had once known another camp cook who had thought Mons., Sig. and Millie (Trans-Mississippi for Mlle.) were Italian given names; this cook used to marvel therefore at the paucity of Neo-Roman precognomens, and therefore why not——

I have said that snow is a test of men. For one day, two days, Étienne stood at the window, Fletcherizing his finger nails and shrieking and moaning at the monotony. To me, Étienne was just about as unbearable as the snow; and so, seeking relief, I went out on the second day to look at my horse, slipped on a stone, broke my collarbone, and thereafter underwent not the snow test, but the test of flat-on-the-back. A test that comes once too often for any man to stand.

However, I bore up cheerfully. I was now merely a spectator, and from my couch in the big room I could lie and watch the human interplay with that detached, impassive, impersonal feeling which French writers tell us is so valuable to the litterateur, and American writers to the faro-dealer.

"I shall go crazy in this abominable, mee-ser-rhable place!" was Étienne's constant prediction.

"Never knew Mark Twain to bore me before," said Ross, over and over. He sat by the other window, hour after hour, a box of Pittsburg stogies of the length, strength, and odour of a Pittsburg graft scandal deposited on one side of him, and "Roughing It," "The Jumping Frog," and "Life on the Mississippi" on the other. For every chapter he lit a new stogy, puffing furiously. This, in time, gave him a recurrent premonition of cramps, gastritis, smoker's colic, or whatever it is they have in Pittsburg after a too deep indulgence in graft scandals. To fend off the colic, Ross resorted time and again to Old Doctor Still's Amber-Coloured U. S. A. Colic Cure. Result, after forty-eight hours—nerves.

"Positive fact I never knew Mark Twain to make me tired before. Positive fact." Ross slammed

"Roughing It" on the floor. "When you're snow-bound this-away you want tragedy, I guess. Humour just seems to bring out all your cussedness. You read a man's poor, pitiful attempts to be funny and it makes you so nervous you want to tear the book up, get out your bandana, and have a good, long cry."

At the other end of the room, the Frenchman took his finger nails out of his mouth long enough to exclaim: "Humour! Humour at such a time as thees! My God, I shall go crazy in thees abominable——"

"Supper," announced George.

These meals were not the meals of Rabelais who said, "the great God makes the planets and we make the platters neat." By that time, the ranch-house meals were not affairs of gusto; they were mental distraction, not bodily provender. What they were to be later shall never be forgotten by Ross or me or Étienne.

After supper, the stogies and finger nails began again. My shoulder ached wretchedly, and with half-closed eyes I tried to forget it by watching the deft movements of the stolid cook.

Suddenly I saw him cock his ear, like a dog. Then, with a swift step, he moved to the door, threw it open, and stood there.

The rest of us had heard nothing.

"What is it, George?" asked Ross.

The cook reached out his hand into the darkness alongside the jamb. With careful precision he prodded something. Then he made one careful step into the snow. His back muscles bulged a little under the arms as he stooped and lightly lifted a burden. Another step inside the door, which he shut methodically behind him, and he dumped the burden at a safe distance from the fire.

He stood up and fixed us with a solemn eye. None of us moved under that Orphic suspense until,

"A woman," remarked George.

Miss Willie Adams was her name. Vocation, school-teacher. Present avocation, getting lost in the snow. Age, yum-yum (the Persian for twenty). Take to the woods if you would describe Miss Adams. A willow for grace; a hickory for fibre; a birch for the clear whiteness of her skin; for eyes, the blue sky seen through treetops; the silk in cocoons for her hair; her voice, the murmur of the evening June wind in the leaves; her mouth, the berries of the wintergreen; fingers as light as ferns; her toe as small as a deer track. General impression upon the dazed beholder —you could not see the forest for the trees.

Psychology, with a capital P and the foot of a lynx, at this juncture stalks into the ranch house. Three men, a cook, a pretty young woman—all snowbound. Count me out of it, as I did not count, anyway. I never did, with women. Count the cook out, if you like. But note the effect upon Ross and Étienne Girod.

Ross dumped Mark Twain in a trunk and locked

the trunk. Also, he discarded the Pittsburg scandals. Also, he shaved off a three days' beard.

Étienne, being French, began on the beard first. He pomaded it, from a little tube of grease Hongroise in his vest pocket. He combed it with a little aluminum comb from the same vest pocket. He trimmed it with manicure scissors from the same vest pocket. His light and Gallic spirits underwent a sudden, miraculous change. He hummed a blithe San Salvador Opera Company tune; he grinned, smirked, bowed, pirouetted, twiddled, twaddled, twisted, and tooralooed. Gayly, the notorious troubadour, could not have equalled Étienne.

Ross's method of advance was brusque, domineering. "Little woman," he said, "you're welcome here!"—and with what he thought subtle double meaning—"welcome to stay here as long as you like, snow or no snow."

Miss Adams thanked him a little wildly, some of the wintergreen berries creeping into the birch bark. She looked around hurriedly as if seeking escape. But there was none, save the kitchen and the room allotted her. She made an excuse and disappeared into her own room.

Later I, feigning sleep, heard the following:

"Mees Adams, I was almos' to perish-die-of monotony w'en your fair and beautiful face appear in thees mee-ser-rhable house." I opened my starboard eye. The beard was being curled furiously around a finger, the Svengali eye was rolling, the chair was

115

being hunched closer to the school-teacher's. "I am French—you see—temperamental—nervous! I cannot endure thees dull hours in thees ranch house; but—a woman comes! Ah!" The shoulders gave nine 'rahs and a tiger. "What a difference! All is light and gay; ever'ting smile w'en you smile. You have 'eart, beauty, grace. My 'eart comes back to me w'en I feel your 'eart. So!" He laid his hand upon his vest pocket. From this vantage point he suddenly snatched at the school-teacher's own hand. "Ah! Mees Adams, if I could only tell you how I ad——"

"Dinner," remarked George. He was standing just behind the Frenchman's ear. His eyes looked straight into the school-teacher's eyes. After thirty seconds of survey, his lips moved, deep in the flinty, frozen maelstrom of his face: "Dinner," he concluded, "will be ready in two minutes."

Miss Adams jumped to her feet, relieved. "I must get ready for dinner," she said brightly, and went into her room.

Ross came in fifteen minutes late. After the dishes had been cleaned away, I waited until a propitious time when the room was temporarily ours alone, and told him what had happened.

He became so excited that he lit a stogy without thinking. "Yeller-hided, unwashed, palm-readin' skunk," he said under his breath. "I'll shoot him full o' holes if he don't watch out—talkin' that way to my wife!"

I gave a jump that set my collarbone back another week. "Your wife!" I gasped.

"Well, I mean to make her that," he announced.

The air in the ranch house the rest of that day was tense with pent-up emotions, oh, best buyers of best sellers.

Ross watched Miss Adams as a hawk does a hen; he watched Étienne as a hawk does a scarecrow. Étienne watched Miss Adams as a weasel does a henhouse. He paid no attention to Ross.

The condition of Miss Adams, in the rôle of sought-after, was feverish. Lately escaped from the agony and long torture of the white cold, where for hours Nature had kept the little school-teacher's vision locked in and turned upon herself, nobody knows through what profound, feminine introspections she had gone. Now, suddenly cast among men, instead of finding relief and security, she beheld herself plunged anew into other discomforts. Even in her own room she could hear the loud voices of her imposed suitors. "I'll blow you full o' holes!" shouted Ross. "Witnesses," shrieked Étienne, waving his hand at the cook and me. She could not have known the previous harassed condition of the men, fretting under indoor conditions. All she knew was, that where she had expected the frank freemasonry of the West, she found the subtle tangle of two men's minds, bent upon exacting whatever romance there might be in her situation.

She tried to dodge Ross and the Frenchman by

spells of nursing me. They also came over to help nurse. This combination aroused such a natural state of invalid cussedness on my part that they all were forced to retire. Once she did manage to whisper: "I am so worried here. I don't know what to do."

To which I replied, gently, hitching up my shoulder, that I was a hunch-savant and that the Eighth House under this sign, the Moon being in Virgo, showed that everything would turn out all right.

But twenty minutes later I saw Étienne reading her palm and felt that perhaps I might have to recast her horoscope, and try for a dark man coming with a bundle.

Toward sunset, Étienne left the house for a few moments and Ross, who had been sitting taciturn and morose, having unlocked Mark Twain, made another dash. It was typical Ross talk.

He stood in front of her and looked down majestically at that cool and perfect spot where Miss Adams' forehead met the neat part in her fragrant hair. First, however, he cast a desperate glance at me. I was in a profound slumber.

"Little woman," he began, "it's certainly tough for a man like me to see you bothered this way. You"—gulp—"you have been alone in this world too long. You need a protector. I might say that at a time like this you need a protector the worst kind— a protector who would take a three-ring delight in smashing the saffron-coloured kisser off of any yellerskinned skunk that made himself obnoxious to you. Hem. Hem. I am a lonely man, Miss Adams. I have so far had to carry on my life without the"— gulp—"sweet radiance"—gulp—"of a woman around the house. I feel especially doggoned lonely at a time like this, when I am pretty near locoed from havin' to stall indoors, and hence it was with delight I welcomed your first appearance in this here shack. Since then I have been packed jam full of more different kinds of feelings, ornery, mean, dizzy, and superb, than has fallen my way in years." Miss Adams made a useless movement toward escape. The Ross chin stuck firm. "I don't want to annoy you, Miss Adams, but, by heck, if it comes to that you'll have to be annoyed. And I'll have to have my say. This palm-ticklin' slob of a Frenchman ought to be kicked off the place and if you'll say the word, off he goes. But I don't want to do the wrong thing. You've got to show a preference. I'm gettin' around to the point, Miss—Miss Willie, in my own brick fashion. I've stood about all I can stand these last two days and somethin's got to happen. The suspense hereabouts is enough to hang a sheepherder. Miss Willie"—he lassooed her hand by main force—"just say the word. You need somebody to take your part all your life long. Will you mar——"

"Supper," remarked George, tersely, from the kitchen door.

Miss Adams hurried away.

Ross turned angrily. "You——"

"I have been revolving it in my head," said George.

He brought the coffeepot forward heavily. Then gravely the big platter of pork and beans. Then sombrely the potatoes. Then profoundly the biscuits. "I been revolving it in my mind. There ain't no use waitin' any longer for Swengalley. Might as well eat now."

From my excellent vantage-point on the couch I watched the progress of that meal. Ross muddled, glowering, disappointed; Étienne, eternally blandishing, attentive, ogling; Miss Adams nervous, picking at her food, hesitant about answering questions, almost hysterical; now and then the solid, flitting shadow of the cook, passing behind their backs like a Dreadnaught in a fog.

I used to own a clock which gurgled in its throat three minutes before it struck the hour. I know, therefore, the slow freight of Anticipation. For I have awakened at three in the morning, heard the clock gurgle and waited those three minutes for the three strokes I knew were to come. *Alors.* In Ross's ranch house that night the slow freight of Climax whistled in the distance.

Étienne began it after supper. Miss Adams had suddenly displayed a lively interest in the kitchen layout and I could see her in there, chatting brightly at George—not with him—the while he ducked his head and rattled his pans.

"My fren'," said Étienne, exhaling a large cloud

120

from his cigarette and patting Ross lightly on the
shoulder with a bediamonded hand which hung limp
from a yard or more of bony arm, "I see I mus' be
frank with you. Firs', because we are rivals; second,
because you take these matters so serious. I—I am
Frenchman. I love the women"—he threw back
his curls, bared his yellow teeth, and blew an un-
savory kiss toward the kitchen. "It is, I suppose,
a trait of my nation. All Frenchmen love the women
—pretty women. Now, look: Here I am!" He
spread out his arms. "Cold outside! I detes' the
col-l-l'! Snow! I abominate the mees-ser-rhable
snow! Two men! This"—pointing to me—"an'
this!" Pointing to Ross. "I am distracted! For
two whole days I stan' at the window an' tear my
'air! I am nervous, upset, pr-r-ro-foun'ly distress
inside my 'ead! An' suddenly—be'old! A woman,
a nice, pretty, charming, innocen' young woman! I,
naturally, rejoice. I become myself again—gay,
light-'earted, 'appy. I address myself to made-
moiselle; it passes the time. That, m'sieu', is wot
the women are for—pass the time! Entertainment—
like the music, like the wine!

"They appeal to the mood, the caprice, the tem-
peramen'. To play with thees woman, follow her
through her humour, pursue her—ah! that is the
mos' delightful way to sen' the hours about their business."

Ross banged the table. "Shut up, you miserable
yeller pup!" he roared. "I object to your pursuin'

anything or anybody in my house. Now, you listen to me, you——" He picked up the box of stogies and used it on the table as an emphasizer. The noise of it awoke the attention of the girl in the kitchen. Unheeded, she crept into the room. "I don't know anything about your French ways of lovemakin', an' I don't care. In my section of the country, it's the best man wins. And I'm the best man here, and don't you forget it! This girl's goin' to be mine. There ain't going to be any playing, or philandering, or palm reading about it. I've made up my mind I'll have this girl, and that settles it. My word is the law in this neck o' the woods. She's mine and as soon as she says she's mine, you pull out." The box made one final, tremendous punctuation point.

Étienne's bravado was unruffled. "Ah! that is no way to win a woman," he smiled, easily. "I make prophecy you will never win 'er that way. No. Not thees woman. She mus' be played along an' then keessed, this charming, delicious little creature. One keess! An' then you 'ave her." Again he displayed his unpleasant teeth. "I make you a bet I will keess her——"

As a cheerful chronicler of deeds done well, it joys me to relate that the hand which fell upon Étienne's amorous lips was not his own. There was one sudden sound, as of a mule kicking a lath fence, and then— through the swinging doors of oblivion for Étienne.

I had seen this blow delivered. It was an aloof, unstudied, almost absent-minded affair. I had thought the cook was rehearsing the proper method of turning a flapjack.

Silently, lost in thought, he stood there scratching his head. Then he began rolling down his sleeves.

"You'd better get your things on, Miss, and we'll get out of here," he decided. "Wrap up warm."

I heard her heave a little sigh of relief as she went to get her cloak, sweater, and hat.

Ross jumped to his feet, and said: "George, what are you goin' to do?"

George, who had been headed in my direction, slowly swivelled around and faced his employer. "Bein' a camp cook, I ain't overburdened with hosses," George enlightened us. "Therefore, I am going to try to borrow this feller's here."

For the first time in four days my soul gave a genuine cheer. "If it's for Lochinvar purposes, go as far as you like," I said grandly.

The cook studied me a moment, as if trying to find an insult in my words. "No," he replied. "It's for mine and the young lady's purposes, and we'll go only three miles—to Hicksville. Now let me tell you somethin', Ross." Suddenly I was confronted with the cook's chunky back and I heard a low, curt carrying voice shoot through the room at my host. George had wheeled just as Ross started to speak. "You're nutty. That's what's the matter with you. You can't stand the snow. You're gettin' nervouser and nuttier every day. That and this Dago"— he jerked a thumb at the half-dead Frenchman in the corner—"has got you to the point where I thought I better horn in. I got to revolvin' it around in my mind and I seen if somethin' wasn't done, and done soon, there'd be murder around here and maybe"—his head gave an imperceptible list toward the girl's room—"worse."

He stopped, but he held up a stubby finger to keep any one else from speaking. Then he plowed slowly through the drift of his ideas. "About this here woman. I know you, Ross, and I know what you reely think about women. If she hadn't happened in here durin' this here snow, you'd never have given two thoughts to the whole woman question. Likewise, when the storm clears, and you and the boys go hustlin' out, this here whole business 'll clear out of your head and you won't think of a skirt again until Kingdom Come. Just because o' this snow here, don't forget you're livin' in the selfsame world you was in four days ago. And you're the same man, too. Now, what's the use o' gettin' all snarled up over four days of stickin' in the house? That there's what I been revolvin' in my mind and this here 's the decision I've come to."

He plodded to the door and shouted to one of the ranch hands to saddle my horse.

Ross lit a stogy and stood thoughtful in the middle of the room. Then he began: "I've a durn good notion, George, to knock your confounded head off and throw you into that snowbank, if——"

"You're wrong, mister. That ain't a durned good

notion you've got. It's durned bad. Look here!"
He pointed steadily out of doors until we were both
forced to follow his finger. "You're in here for
more'n a week yet." After allowing this fact to
sink in, he barked out at Ross: "Can *you* cook?"
Then at me: "Can *you* cook?" Then he looked at
the wreck of Étienne and sniffed.

There was an embarrassing silence as Ross and I
thought solemnly of a foodless week.

"If you just use hoss sense," concluded George,
"and don't go for to hurt my feelin's, all I want to do
is to take this young gal down to Hicksville; and then
I'll head back here and cook fer you."

The horse and Miss Adams arrived simultaneously,
both of them very serious and quiet. The horse
because he knew what he had before him in that
weather; the girl because of what she had left behind.

Then all at once I awoke to a realization of what
the cook was doing. "My God, man!" I cried,
"aren't you afraid to go out in that snow?"

Behind my back I heard Ross mutter, "Not him."

George lifted the girl daintily up behind the saddle,
drew on his gloves, put his foot in the stirrup, and
turned to inspect me leisurely.

As I passed slowly in his review, I saw in my mind's
eye the algebraic equation of Snow, the equals sign,
and the answer in the man before me.

"Snow is my last name," said George. He swung
into the saddle and they started cautiously out into
the darkening swirl of fresh new currency just issuing

from the Snowdrop Mint. The girl, to keep her place, clung happily to the sturdy figure of the camp cook.

I brought three things away from Ross Curtis's ranch house—yea, four. One was the appreciation of snow, which I have so humbly tried here to render; (2) was a collarbone, of which I am extra careful; (3) was a memory of what it is to eat very extremely terribly bad food for a week; and (4) was the cause of (3) a little note delivered at the end of the week and hand-painted in blue pencil on a sheet of meat paper.

"I cannot come back there to that there job. Mrs. Snow say no, George. I been revolvin' it in my mind; considerin' circumstances she's right."

PART II

CRITICAL AND BIOGRAPHICAL COMMENT

LITTLE PICTURES OF O. HENRY
By Arthur W. Page

Part I—Born and Raised in No'th Ca'lina

IN GREENSBORO, North Carolina, at the time of Will Porter's youth there were four classes of people: decent white folks, mean white folks, decent "niggers," and mean "niggers." Will Porter and his people belonged to the first class. During the time that he was growing up there were about twenty-five hundred people in Greensboro. It was a simple, democratic little place with rather more intellectual ambitions than most places of its size, but without the hum of modern industry which the cotton mills have latterly brought to it or the great swarm of eager students that now flock to the State Normal School.

In this quiet and pleasant community William Sydney Porter grew up. Algernon Sidney Porter, his father, was a doctor of skill and distinction, who in late life practised his profession little, but worked upon many inventions. His mother is said to have written poetry and her father was at one time editor of the Greensboro *Patriot*. A President, a planter, a banker, a blacksmith, a short-story writer or a sailor might any of them have such forbears as these. If any dependence can be laid upon early "in-

129

fluences" that affect an author's work, in O. Henry's case we must certainly consider Aunt "Lina" Porter. She attended to his bringing up at home and he attended her instruction at school. His mother died when Will Porter was very young, and his aunt, Miss Evelina Porter, ran the Porter household as well as the school next door, and a most remarkable school it was.

Porter's desk-mate in that school, Tom Tate, not long ago wrote the following account, for his niece to read:

"Miss Porter was a maiden lady and conducted a private school on West Market Street, in Greensboro, adjoining the Porter residence. Will was educated there, and this was his whole school education (with the exception of a term or two at graded school). There was a great deal more learned in this little one-story, one-roomed school house than the three R's. It was the custom of 'Miss Lina,' as every one called her, during the recess hour to read aloud to those of her scholars who cared to hear her, and there was always a little group around her chair listening. She selected good books, and a great many of her old scholars showed the impress of these little readings in after life. On Friday night there was a gathering of the scholars at her home, and those were good times, too. They ate roasted chestnuts, popped corn or barbecued quail and rabbits before the big open wood fire in her room. There was always a book to read or a story to be told. Then there was a game of story-telling, one of the gathering would start the

story and each one of the others was called on in turn
to add his quota until the end. Miss Lina's and
Will's were always interesting. In the summer time
there were picnics and fishing expeditions; in the
autumn chinquapin and hickory gatherings; and in
the spring wild-flower hunts, all personally conducted
by Miss Lina.

"During these days Will showed decided artistic
talent, and it was predicted that he would follow in
the footsteps of his kinsman, Tom Worth, the cartoonist, but the literary instinct was there, too, and
the quaint dry humour and the keen insight into the
peculiarities of human nature.

"The boys of the school were divided in two clubs,
the Brickbats and the Union Jacks. The members
of the Union Jacks were Percy Gray, Will Porter, Jim
Doak, and Tom Tate, three of whom died before
reaching middle age. Tom Tate is the sole survivor
of this little party of four.

"This club had headquarters in an outbuilding on
the grounds of the old Edgeworth Female College,
which some years previously had been destroyed by
fire. In this house they kept their arms and accou-
trements, consisting of wooden battle-axes, shields,
and old cavalry sabres, and on Friday nights it was
their custom to sally forth armed and equipped in
search of adventure, like knights of old from their
castle, carefully avoiding the dark nooks where the
moonlight did not fall. Will was the leading spirit
in these daring pursuits, and many was the hair-

raising adventure these ten-year-old heroes encountered, and the shields and battle-axes were oft-times
thrown aside so as not to impede the free action of
the nether limbs when safety lay only in flight.
Ghosts were of common occurrence in those days, or
rather nights, and arms were useless to cope with the
supernatural; it took good sturdy legs.

"In the summer an occasional banquet was spread
on the moss and grass under the spreading branches
of the old oaks that surrounded the club house. On
one such festal gathering ginger cakes and lemonade
constituted the refreshments. The lemonade was
made in a tub furnished by Percy Gray, and during
the after-dinner talks one of the Sir Knights impru-
dently asked if the tub was a new one, and Percy
replied in an injured tone: 'Why, of course it is;
papa has only bathed in it three times.' To use an
old quotation, 'Ah! then and there was hurrying to
and fro and blanching of red lips and so forth.' . . .

"After the short school-days Porter found employment as prescription clerk in the drugstore of his
uncle, Clarke Porter, and it was there that his genius
as an artist and writer budded forth and gave the
first promise of the work of after years. The old
Porter drugstore was the social club of the town in
those days. A game of chess went on in the back
room always, and around the old stove behind the
prescription counter the judge, the colonel, the doctor,
and other local celebrities gathered and discussed affairs of state, the fate of nations, and other things, and

incidentally helped themselves to liberal portions of Clarke's Vini Gallaci or smoked his cigars without money and without price. There were some rare characters who gathered around that old stove, some queer personalities, and Porter caught them and transferred them to paper by both pen and pencil in an illustrated comedy satire that was his first public literary and artistic effort.

"When this was read and shown around the stove the picture was so true to life and caught the peculiarities of the *dramatis personæ* so aptly it was some time before the young playwright was on speaking terms with some of his old friends. 'Alias Jimmy Valentine's' hit* is history now, but I doubt if at any time there was a more genuine tribute to Porter's ability than from the audience around the old stove, behind the prescription counter nearly thirty years ago.

"In those days Sunday was a day of rest, and Porter with a friend would spend the long afternoons out on some sunny hillside sheltered from the wind by the thick brown broom sedge, lying on their backs gazing up into the blue sky dreaming, planning, talking, or turning to their books, reading. He was an ardent lover of God's great out-of-doors, a dreamer, a thinker, and a constant reader. He was such a man —true-hearted and steadfast to those he cared for, as gentle and sensitive as a woman, retiring to a fault, pure, clean, and honourable."

---

* This play is the dramatized version of A Retrieved Reformation. (See "Roads of Destiny.")

In these characteristics Will Porter followed in his father's footsteps. It was a saying in Greensboro that if there were cushioned seats in Heaven old Dr. Porter would have one, because of his charity and goodness to the poor. And there was an active sympathy between the old man and his son. The old gentleman on cold stormy nights when his boy was late getting home from the drugstore always had a roaring wood fire for him, and a pot of coffee and potatoes and eggs warming in the fire for his midnight supper.

This timid, quiet lad, who would slip around to the back door of Miss "Lina's," if there was company in the front of the house, held a little court of his own at the drugstore. He was the delight and pride of men two and three times his age. They still talk of the pictures he drew, the quiet pranks he played; but their greatest pride in him, as indicated above, is as a playwright. If you find one of that group now, and speak of O. Henry he will ask: "Did you ever hear of the play Will wrote when he was sixteen?" and then he will launch into laughing description of the little play written thirty-five years ago.

His pencil was busy most of the time, if not with writing, with drawing. He was a famous cartoonist. There are several versions of the story about him and an important customer at his uncle's store. Young Porter did not remember the customer's name, but when the man asked him to charge some articles he did not wish to admit his ignorance. So he put down the items and drew a picture of the customer. His uncle had no difficulty in recognizing the likeness. Perhaps one of the other versions of this story is the true one, but as they all unite upon the fact that he made a likeness that was accurate enough for his uncle to base his accounts upon, we may be certain that during his drug-store-club days young Porter was an adept at pencil mimicry as well as personal playwriting. It is as certain, too, that he dearly loved practical jokes. According to Mr. Charles Benbow, of Greensboro, "there was an old darkey by the name of Pink Lindsay who swept out the drug-store, made fires, and so forth. He was very fond of whiskey, and it took great care on the part of Will Porter and Ed Michaux, clerks, to keep Pink away from the whiskey used in prescriptions. They had a barrel of whiskey in the cellar and used a rubber tube to syphon the whiskey out of the barrel into a big bottle which was kept at the prescription counter. Notwithstanding the fact that the rubber tube was kept under lock and key old Pink or somebody was getting the whiskey. One day Will was in the cellar having Pink clean up the rubbish, and while sweeping down cobwebs he discovered two long straws hid on the wall of earth near the whiskey barrel. He said nothing. When Pink was out he examined the barrel and discovered a small hole bored into the top near the end of the cask. Immediately he divined how and where the whiskey went. He quietly took the straws upstairs and filled them with capsicum. He put them back exactly where he had found them. In those days we did not need pure food laws—capsicum was red pepper genuine. Pink was kept out of the cellar all day. The next morning being a cold one, Pink was both dry and cold. When Will sent him down cellar he was more than ready to comply. The cellar door opened out on the sidewalk and was one of those folding doors that when closed down act as a part of the sidewalk. It is usually closed as one goes down cellar. This time Pink happened to leave it open, and it was well for him. A few minutes elapsed and he let out a howl that would have done credit to a Comanche Indian. Yelling that he was poisoned, he made a bee line for the pump out in the street. Will pumped water for him until he could talk, and then he pumped the truth out of Pink about the straws. He was 'pizened,' and he was afire, and he promised never to use the straws again. All the while Will was as sober as a judge. He never smiled, and Pink did not suspect him."

In 1882 Dr. and Mrs. J. K. Hall went to Texas to visit their sons, Richard and Lee Hall, of Texas-ranger fame, and Will Porter was sent with them, because it was thought that the close confinement in the drugstore was undermining his health. He never again lived in Greensboro, but Greensboro was never altogether out of his mind. Many years later, when he was living in New York, he wrote this account of himself—an account which gives an inkling of the whimsical charm of the man and his fondness for the old life in the old land of his birth.

"I take my pen in hand to say that I am from the South and have been a stranger in New York for four years. I am sometimes full of sunshine and at other times about as cross and disagreeable as you ever see 'em. But I know a restaurant where you can get real Corn Bread, clean, respectable, cozy, and draw the line at two things. I will not go to Coney Island and will not take walks on Sunday afternoons.

"It's a hard task to tell about one's self, for if you say too much you get turned down for an egoist, and if you don't say enough the man with the black moustache and side-bar buggy gets ahead of you.

"Now for something very personal and thrilling. It's about me."

(*The following paragraph was cut from a newspaper and pasted on the letter.*)

"'He is a true soldier of fortune. He is still a very young man, but he has lived a varied life. He has been a cowboy, sheepherder, merchant, salesman, miner, and a great many other nameless things in the course of a number of very full years spent doing our West, Southwest, Mexico, South and Central America. He went about with a keen eye and supplemented it with a ready notebook, into which he jotted down his impressions and things that happened his way.'

"There are a few misstatements in the excerpt.

I am not a 'very young man.' Wish I was. I have
never been a cowboy, sheepherder, merchant, salesman, or miner. But I lived 'on the ground' with
cowboys for two years. I never carried a notebook
in my life. But here I plead guilty."

(*Here follows another newspaper clipping.*)

"'He carried an abundant good fellowship and
humour with him and saw the bright and amusing
side of things.'

"Don't forget that I am the only original dispenser
of sunshine.

"You may notice that I suppress my pen name in
the quotations. I do that because I have been trying to keep my personality separate from my *nom
de guerre* except from my intimate friends and
publishers.

"I was born and raised in 'No'th Ca'lina' and at
eighteen went to Texas and ran wild on the prairies.
Wild yet, but not so wild. Can't get to loving New
Yorkers. Live all alone in a great big two rooms on
quiet old Irving Place three doors from Wash. Irving's old home. Kind of lonesome. Was thinking
lately (since the April moon commenced to shine)
how I'd like to be down South, where I could happen
over to Miss Ethel's or Miss Sallie's and sit on the
porch—not on a chair—on the edge of the porch, and
lay my straw hat on the steps and lay my head back
against the honeysuckle on the post—and just talk.
And Miss Ethel would go in directly (they say presently up here) and bring out the guitar. She would

complain that the E string was broken, but no one would believe her, and pretty soon all of us would be singing the 'Swanee River' and 'In the Evening by the Moonlight' and—oh, gol darn it, what's the use of wishing.''

PART II—TEXAN DAYS

Will Porter found a new kind of life in Texas—a life that filled his mind with that rich variety of types and adventures which later was translated into his stories. Here he got—from observation, and not from experience, as has often been said, for he was never a cowboy—the originals of his Western characters and Western scenes. He looked on at the more picturesque life about him rather than shared in it; though through his warm sympathy and his vivid imagination he entered into its spirit as completely as any one who had fully lived its varied parts.

It was while he was living on the Hall ranch, to which he had gone in search of health, that he wrote —and at once destroyed—his first stories of Western life. And it was there, too, that he drew the now famous series of illustrations for a book that never was printed. The author of that book, "Uncle Joe" Dixon, was a prospector in the bonanza mining days in Colorado. Now he is a newspaper editor in Florida; and he has lately told, for the survivors of Will Porter's friends of that period, the story of the origin of these drawings. His narrative illustrates anew the remarkable impression that Will Porter's quaint and whimsical personality, even in his boyhood, made upon those who knew him.

Other friends, who knew him more intimately than "Uncle Joe" Dixon, saw other sides of Will Porter's character. With them his boyish love of fun and of good-natured and sometimes daredevil mischief came again to the surface, as well as those refinements of feeling and manner that were his heritage as one of the "decent white folks" of Greensboro. And with them, too, came out the ironical fate that pursued him most of his life—to be a dreamer and yet to be harnessed to tasks that brought his head from the clouds to the commonplaces of the store and the street. Perhaps it was this very bending of a sky-seeking imagination to the dusty comedy of every day that brought him later to see life as he pictured it in "The Four Million," with its mingling of Caliph Haroun-al-Raschid's romance with the adventures of shop girls and restaurant-keepers. At any rate, even the Texas of the drug-clerk days and of the bank-clerk period appealed to his sense of the humorous and romantic and grotesque. Here is what one intimate of those days recalls of his character and exploits:

"Will Porter, shortly after coming to Texas, became a member of the Hill City Quartette, of Austin, composed of C. E. Hillyer, R. H. Edmundson, Howard Long, and himself. Porter was the littlest man in the crowd, and, of course, basso profundo. He was about five feet six inches tall, weighed about one hundred and thirty pounds, had coal black hair, gray eyes, and a long, carefully twisted moustache; looked as though he might be a combination between the French and the Spanish, and I think he once told me that the blood of the Huguenot flowed in his veins. He was one of the most accomplished gentlemen I ever knew. His voice was soft and musical, with just enough rattle in it to rid it of all touch of effeminacy. He had a keen sense of humour, and there were two distinct methods of address which were characteristic with him—his business address and his friendly address. As a business man, his face was calm, almost expressionless; his demeanour was steady, even calculated. He always worked for a high class of employers, was never wanting for a position, and was prompt, accurate, talented, and very efficient; but the minute he was out of business —that was all gone. He always approached a friend with a merry twinkle in his eye and an expression which said: 'Come on, boys, we are going to have a lot of fun,' and we usually did.

"The story of The Green Door* in its spirit and in its fact was just such a thing as might happen with him any night. It is but justice, in order to give balance to this unique character, to say that he made no religious professions; he never talked infidelity nor scepticism; he had such a reverence for other people's views that he never entered into religious discussions; and personally he seemed rather indif-

* See "The Four Million."

ferent to the subject, though in no wise opposed to it. He rarely ever missed church, and the Hill City Quartette were nearly always to be found in either the Baptist or the St. David's Episcopal Church choirs, though he usually attended church on Sunday evenings at the Presbyterian Church and sang in their choir.

"He got interested in society and lost all taste for the drug business. Being a fine penman, a good accountant, well educated, and with good address, it was an easy matter for him to make a living without working every day and Sunday, too, and most of the evenings besides. The fact of the matter is, while W. S. P. would not have admitted it for the world, I think he really wanted a little more time for love-making. So during the time of our association, he went to work at eight in the morning and quit at four. He always had sufficient money for what he needed; if he had any more, no one knew it. He was very fond of going fishing, but he let you do the fishing after he went. He loved to go hunting, but he let you kill the birds, and somehow I always thought that on these trips he got something out of the occasion that he enjoyed all by himself; they were not occasions which invited the introduction of sentiment, yet I believe his enjoyment of them was purely sentimental. He loved the mountains and the plains; he loved to hear the birds sing and the brooks babble, and all those things, but he did not talk to the boys about it.

"He was accomplished in all the arts of a society

man; had a good bass voice and sang well; was a good dancer and skater; played an interesting game of cards, and was preëminently an entertainer. There were no wall flowers to Porter, and the girl who went with him never lacked for attention.

"The Hill City Quartette formed the centre of the Social Circle in which W. S. P. was the central figure during the period of this writing.

"If W. S. P. at this time had any ambitions as a writer, he never mentioned it to me. I do not recall that he was fond of reading. One day I quoted some lines to him from a poem by John Alexander Smith. He made inquiry about the author, borrowed the book, and committed to memory a great many passages from it, but I do not recall ever having known him to read any other book. I asked him one day why he never read fiction. His reply was: 'That it was all tame compared with the romance in his own life,'—which was really true.

"Mr. Porter was very careful in the use and selection of language. He rarely used slang, and his style in ordinary conversation was very much purer and more perfect than it is in his writings. This can be accounted for in the fact that he was an unusually polished gentleman, but writing in the first person, the character which he selects to represent himself appears to be along a much lower and commoner line than he himself actually lived; but, on the other hand, the stories that he writes and the quaint way he has of putting things were largely characteristic of his personal daily life, and the peculiar turn that he gives to his stories—in which he leads you to think along logical lines until you think you have anticipated his conclusion, then suddenly brings the story to a reasonable but wholly unexpected conclusion— was even in this early day an element in his common conversation.

"In the great railroad strike at Fort Worth, Texas, the Governor called out the State Militia, and the company to which we belonged was sent, but as we were permitted a choice in the matter, Porter and I chose not to go. In a little while a girl he was in love with went to Waco on a visit. Porter moped around disconsolate for a few days, and suddenly said to me: 'I believe I'll take a visit at the Government's expense.' With him to think was to act. A telegram was sent to Fort Worth: 'Capt. Blank, Fort Worth, Texas. Squad of volunteers Company Blank, under my command, tender you their services if needed. Reply.' 'Come next train,' Captain Blank commanded. Upon reaching the depot no orders for transportation of squad had been received. Porter actually held up the train until he could telegraph and get transportation for his little squad, because the girl had been notified that he would be in Waco on a certain train. She afterward said that when the train pulled into Waco he was sitting on the engine pilot with a gun across his lap and a distant glance at her was all that he got, but he had had his adventure and was fully repaid.

"This adventure is only one of thousands of such incidents that commonly occurred in his life. He lived in an atmosphere of adventure that was the product of his own imagination. He was an inveterate story-teller, seemingly purely from the pleasure of it, but he never told a vulgar joke, and as much as he loved humour he would not sacrifice decency for its sake, and his stories about women were always refined.

"He told a great many stories in the first person. We were often puzzled to know whether they were real or imaginary, and when we made inquiry his stock reply was: 'Never question the validity of a joke.'

"One night at the Lampasas Military Encampment of Texas Volunteer Guards, the Quartette, with others, had leave of absence to attend the big ball at the Park Hotel, with orders to report at 12:00 sharp. Somehow, with girls and gaiety and music and balmy Southern breezes and cooing voices, time flies, and before any of us had thought to look at a watch it was five minutes past twelve and we were in trouble. We had all gathered near the doorway looking toward Camp when we saw the Corporal of the Guard approaching the building to arrest us. Of course, what follows could never have happened in a camp of tried veterans, but Porter knew the human animal as few people do. He got a friend with an unlimited leave of absence to meet the Corporal's squad at another door and suggest to them that they should not carry the guns in among the ladies. So the squad stacked their guns on the outside and went into the other door to arrest us. Up to this point Porter had worked the thing without taking us into his confidence. As soon as the guns were stacked he beckoned to us to follow and we did not stop for explanation. We knew where Porter led there would be adventure, if not success. He took command; we unstacked the arms of the corporal's squad; all our boys who did not carry guns were marched as under arrest. Now none of us knew the countersign, and our success in getting by the sentry was a matter of pure grit. As we approached the sentry we were crossing a narrow plank bridge in single file, at the end of which the sentry threw up his gun and Porter marched us right straight up to that gun until the front man was marking time with the point of the gun right against his stomach. Porter just said to the sentry, 'Squad under arrest. Stand aside!' The whole thing was done with such courage, decision, and audacity, that the sentry never noticed that we had not given the countersign, but stepped aside and let us pass. A few yards into the camp we stacked our guns, and sneaked into our tents. When the real corporal and squad came back to camp and told his story the sentry refused to accept it and had the whole squad placed in the guardhouse for the night. When the boys began to whisper the joke to their comrades in their tents, the disturbance became so great that the Corporal's Guard came down to ascertain the cause of the disturbance, but in looking into the tent found only tired soldier boys snoring as though they had been drugged. There was quite a time at the court-martial next morning, at which the Corporal and his body were given extra duty for their inglorious behaviour on the previous night, but no one ever knew our connection with the story."

But the lure of the pen was getting too strong for Will Porter to resist. Life as a teller in the First National Bank of Austin was too routine not to be relieved by some outlet for his love of fun and for his creative literary instinct. An opportunity opened to buy a printing outfit, and he seized it and used it for a year to issue the *Rolling Stone*, a weekly paper that suggested even then his later method as a humourist and as a photographic portrayer of odd types of humanity. Dr. D. Daniels—"Dixie" he was to Will Porter—now a dentist in Galveston, Texas, was his partner in this enterprise, and his story of that year of fun gives also a picture of Will Porter's habit of studying human nature at first hand—a habit that later carried him into many quaint byways of New York and into many even more quaint and revealing byways of the human heart. Here is Dr. Daniels's story:

"It was in the spring of 1894 that I floated into Austin," said Daniels, "and I got a place in the State printing office. I had been working there for a short time when I heard that a man named Porter had bought out the old *Iconoclast* plant—known everywhere as Brann's *Iconoclast*—and was looking for a

printer to go into the game with him. I went around
to see him, and that was the first time I met O. Henry.
Porter had been a clerk in the Texas Land Office and a
teller in the First National Bank in Austin, and when
W. C. Brann went to Waco decided to buy out his
plant and run a weekly humorous paper.

"I talked things over with him, the proposition
looked good, and we formed a partnership then and
there. We christened the paper the *Rolling Stone*
after a few discussions, and in smaller type across
the full-page head we printed 'Out for the moss.'
Which is exactly what we were out for. Our idea
was to run this weekly with a lot of current events
treated in humorous fashion, and also to run short
sketches, drawings, and verse. I had been doing a
lot of chalk-plate work and the specimens I showed
seemed to make a hit with Porter. Those chalk-
plates were the way practically all of our cuts were
printed.

"Porter was one of the most versatile men I had
ever met. He was a fine singer, could write remark-
ably clever stuff under all circumstances, and was a
good hand at sketching. And he was the best mimic
I ever saw in my life. He was one of the genuine
democrats that you hear about more often than you
meet. Night after night, after we would shut up
shop, he would call to me to come along and 'go
bumming.' That was his favourite expression for
the night-time prowling in which we indulged. We
would wander through streets and alleys, meeting with

some of the worst specimens of down-and-outers it has ever been my privilege to see at close range. I've seen the most ragged specimen of a bum hold up Porter, who would always do anything he could for the man. His one great failing was his inability to say 'No' to a man.

"He never cared for the so-called 'higher classes' but watched the people on the streets and in the shops and cafés, getting his ideas from them night after night. I think that it was in this way he was able to picture the average man with such marvellous fidelity.

"Well, as I started to say, we moved into the old *Iconoclast* plant, got out a few issues, and moved into the Brueggerhoff Building. The *Rolling Stone* met with unusual success at the start, and we had in our files letters from men like Bill Nye and John Kendrick Bangs praising us for the quality of the sheet. We were doing nicely, getting the paper out every Saturday—approximately—and blowing the gross receipts every night. Then we began to strike snags. One of our features was a series of cuts with humorous underlines of verse. One of the cuts was the rear view of a fat German professor leading an orchestra, beating the air wildly with his baton. Underneath the cut Porter had written the following verse:

> With his baton the professor beats the bars,
> 'Tis also said he beats them when he treats.
> But it made that German gentleman see stars
> When the bouncer got the cue to bar the beats.

"For some reason or other that issue alienated every German in Austin from the *Rolling Stone*, and cost us more than we were able to figure out in subscriptions and advertisements.

"Another mistake Porter made was when he let himself be dragged into a San Antonio political fight —the O'Brien-Callaghan mayoralty campaign. He was pulled into this largely through a broken-down English writer, whose name, as I remember, was Henry Rider Taylor. How Taylor had any influence over him I never was able to make out, for he used constantly to make fun of him. 'Here comes that man Taylor,' he'd say. 'Got a diamond on him as big as a two-bit piece and shinin' like granulated sugar.' But he went into the political scrap just the same, and it cost him more than it was worth.

"We got out one feature of the paper that used to meet with pretty general approval. It was a page gotten up in imitation of a backwoods country paper, and we christened it *The Plunkville Patriot*. That idea has been carried out since then in a dozen different forms, like *The Hogwallow Kentuckian*, and *The Bingville Bugle*, to give two of the prominent examples. Porter and I used to work on this part of the paper nights and Sundays. I would set the type for it, as there was a system to all of the typographical errors that we made, and I couldn't trust any one else to set it up as we wanted it.

"Porter used to think up some right amusing features for this part of the paper. I remember that about then we had on hand a lot of cuts of Gilmore, of Gilmore's Band, which played at the dedication of the State capitol at Austin. We would run these cuts of Gilmore for any one, from Li Hung Chang to Governor Hogg.

"The Populist Party was coming in for all sorts of publicity at this time, and the famous 'Sockless' Simpson, of Kansas, was running for Congress. Porter worked out a series of 'Tictocq, the Great French Detective,' in burlesque of 'Lecoq,' and in one story, I remember, had a deep-laid conspiracy to locate a pair of socks in Simpson's luggage, thus discrediting him with his political following.

"The paper ran along for something over a year, and then was discontinued. Following the political trouble and the other troubles in which Porter became involved, he left the State. Some time was spent in Houston; the next stop was New Orleans; then he jumped to South America, and only returned to Texas for a short period before leaving the State forever. His experiences on a West Texas ranch, in Texas cities and in South America, however, gave him a thorough insight into the average run of people whom he pictured so vividly in his later work. He was a greater man than any of us knew when we were with him in the old days."

III—THE NEW YORK DAYS—*Richard Duffy's narrative*

His coming to New York, with the resolution "to write for bread," as he said once in a mood of acrid

humour, was dramatic, as is a whisper compared to a
subdued tumult of voices. I believe I am correct in
saying that outside his immediate family few were
aware that O. Henry was entering this "nine-day
town" except Gilman Hall, my associate on *Ainslee's
Magazine*, the publishers, Messrs. Street and Smith,
and myself. For some time we had been buying
stories from him, written in his perfect Spencerian
copperplate hand that was to become familiar to so
many editors. Only then he wrote always with a pen
on white paper, whereas once he was established in
New York he used a lead pencil sharpened to a
needle's point on one of the yellow pads that were
always to be seen on his table. The stories he published at this period were laid either in the Southwest
or in Central America, and those of the latter countries
form the bulk of his first issued volume, "Cabbages
and Kings." It was because we were sure of him as a
writer that our publishers willingly advanced the
cheque that brought him to New York and assured
him a short breathing spell to look round and settle.
Also, it was because O. Henry wanted to come.
You could always make him do anything he wanted to
do, as he had a way of saying, if you were coaxing him
into an invitation he had no intention of pursuing into
effect.

It was getting late on a fine spring afternoon down
at Duane and William streets when he came to meet
us. From the outer gate the boy presented a card
bearing the name William Sydney Porter. I don't

remember just when we found out that "O. Henry"
was merely a pen name; but think it was during the
correspondence arranging that he come to New York.
I do remember, however, that when we were preparing our yearly prospectus, we had written to him,
asking that he tell us what the initial O. stood for, as
we wished to use his photograph and preferred to
have his name in full. It was the custom and would
make his name stick faster in the minds of readers.
With a courteous flourish of appreciation at the
honour we were offering him in making him known to
the world, he sent us "Olivier," and so he appeared as
Olivier Henry in the first publishers' announcement
in which his stories were heralded. Later he confided
to us, smiling, what a lot of fun he had had in picking
out a first name of sufficient advertising effectiveness
that began with O.

As happens in these matters, whatever mind picture Gilman Hall or I had formed of him from his
letters, his handwriting, his stories, vanished before
the impression of the actual man. He wore a dark
suit of clothes, I recall, and a four-in-hand tie of
bright colour. He carried a black derby, high-
crowned, and walked with a springy, noiseless step.
To meet him for the first time you felt his most notable quality to be reticence, not a reticence of social
timidity, but a reticence of deliberateness. If you
also were observing, you would soon understand that
his reticence proceeded from the fact that civilly
yet masterfully he was taking in every item of the

"you" being presented to him to the accompaniment of convention's phrases and ideas, together with the "you" behind this presentation. It was because he was able thus to assemble and sift all the multifarious elements of a personality with sleight-of-hand swiftness that you find him characterizing a person or a neighbourhood in a sentence or two; and once I heard him characterize a list of editors he knew each in a phrase.

On his first afternoon in New York we took him on our usual walk uptown from Duane Street to about Madison Square. That was a long walk for O. Henry, as any who knew him may witness. Another long one was when he walked about a mile over a fairly high hill with me on a zigzag path through autumn woods. I showed him plains below us and hills stretching away so far and blue they looked like the illimitable sea from the deck of an ocean liner. But it was not until we approached the station from which we were to take the train back to New York that he showed the least sign of animation. "What's the matter, Bill," I asked, "I thought you'd like to see some real country." His answer was: "Kunn'l, how kin you expeck me to appreciate the glories of nature when you walk me over a mounting like that an' I got new shoes on?" Then he stood on one foot and on the other, caressing each aching member for a second or two, and smiled with bashful knowingness so like him.

It was one of his whimsical amusements, I must

say here, to speak in a kind of country style of English, as though the English language were an instrument he handled with hesitant unfamiliarity. Thus it happened that a woman who had written to him about his stories and asked if her "lady friend" and she might meet him, informed him afterward: "You mortified me nearly to death, you talked so ungrammatical!"

We never knew just where he stopped the first night in New York, beyond his statement that it was at a hotel not far from the ferry in a neighbourhood of so much noise that he had not been able to sleep. I suppose we were voluminous with suggestions as to where he might care to live, because we felt we had some knowledge of the subject of board and lodging, and because he was the kind of man you'd give your best hat to on short acquaintance, if he needed a hat—but also he was the kind of man who would get a hat for himself. Within about twenty-four hours he called at the office again to say that he had taken a large room in a French table d'hôte hotel in Twenty-fourth Street, between Broadway and Sixth Avenue. Moreover, he brought us a story. In those days he was very prolific. He wrote not only stories, but occasional skits and light verse. In a single number of *Ainslee's*, as I remember, we had three short stories of his, one of which was signed "O. Henry" and the other two with pseudonyms. Of the latter, While the Auto Waits,* was picked out

* See "Voice of the City".

by several newspapers outside New York as an unusually clever short story. But as O. Henry naturally he appeared most frequently, as frequently as monthly publication allows, for to my best recollection of the many stories we saw of his there were only three about which we said to him, we would rather have another instead.

Still he lived in West Twenty-fourth Street, although the place had no particular fascination for him. We used to see him every other day or so, at luncheon, at dinner, or in the evening. Various magazine editors began to look up O. Henry, which was a job somewhat akin to tracing a lost person. While his work was coming under general notice rapidly, he made no effort to push himself into general acquaintance; and all who knew him when he was actually somewhat of a celebrity should be able to say that it was about as easy to induce him to "go anywhere" to meet somebody as it is to have a child take medicine. He was persuaded once to be the guest of a member of the Periodical Publishers' Association on a sail up the Hudson; but when the boat made a stop at Poughkeepsie, O. Henry slipped ashore and took the first train back to New York. Yet he was not unsociable, but a man that liked a few friends round him and who dreaded and avoided a so-called "party" as he did a crowd in the subway.

It was at his Twenty-fourth Street room that Robert H. Davis, then of the staff of the New York *World*, ran him to cover, as it were, and concluded a contract with him to furnish one story a week for a year at a fixed salary. It was a gigantic task to face, and I have heard of no other writer who put the same quality of effort and material in his work able to produce one story every seven days for fifty-two successive weeks. The contract was renewed, I believe, and all during this time O. Henry was selling stories to magazines as well. His total of stories amount to two hundred and fifty-one, and when it is considered that they were written in about eight years, one may give him a good mark for industry, especially as he made no professional vaunt about "loving his work." Once, when dispirited, he said that almost any other way of earning a living was less of a toil than writing. The mood is common to writers, but not so common as to happen to a man who practically had editors or agents of editors sitting on his doorstep requesting copy.

When he undertook his contract with the *World* he moved to have more room and more comfortable surroundings for the new job. But he did not move far, no farther than across Madison Square, in East Twenty-fourth Street, to a house near Fourth Avenue. Across the street stands the Metropolitan Building, although it was not so vast then. He had a bedroom and sitting-room at the rear of the parlour floor with a window that looked out on a typical New York yard, boasting one ailanthus tree frowned upon by time-stained extension walls of other houses. More and more men began to seek him out, and he was glad to see them, for a good deal of loneliness enters into the life of a man that writes fiction during the better part of the day, and when his work is over feels he must move about somewhere to gather new material. Here it was that he received a visit one day from a stranger, who announced that he was a business man, but had decided to change his line. He meant to write stories, and having read several of O. Henry's, he was convinced that kind of story would be the best paying proposition. O. Henry liked the man off-hand, but he could not help being amused at his attitude toward a "literary career." I asked what advice he gave the visitor, and he answered: "I told him to go ahead!" The sequel no doubt O. Henry thoroughly enjoyed, for within a few years the stranger had become a best-seller, and continues such.

O. Henry remained only for a few months in these lodgings, having among a dozen reasons for moving the fact that he had more money.

I follow his movings with his trunks, his bags, his books, a few, but books he read, and his pictures, likewise a few, that were original drawings presented to him, or some familiar printed picture that had caught his fancy, because in his movings you trace his life in New York. His next abiding-place was at 55 Irving Place, as he has said in a letter, "a few doors from old Wash. Irving's house." Here he had almost the entire parlour floor with a window large as a store front, opening only at the sides in long panels. At either one of these panels he would sit for hours watching the world go by along the street, not gazing idly, but noting men and women with penetrating eyes, making guesses at what they did for a living, and what fun they got out of it when they had earned it.

He was a man you could sit with a long while and feel no necessity for talking; but ever so often a passerby would evoke a remark from him that converted an iota of humanity into the embryo of a story. Although he spoke hardly ever to any one in the house except the people who managed it, he had the lodgers all ticketed in his mind. He was friendly but distant with persons of the neighbourhood he was bound to meet regularly, because he lived so long there, and I have often thought he must have persisted as a mysterious man to them simply because he was so far from being communicative.

From Irving Place he went back across the Square to live in a house next to the rectory of Trinity Chapel in West Twenty-fifth Street. But now he moved because the landlady and several lodgers were moving to the same house. From here his next change was to the Caledonia, in West Twenty-sixth Street, whence, as everybody knows, he made his last move to the Polyclinic Hospital, where he died.

PART IV—As He Showed Himself in His Letters

Collections of material about an author are not respecters of chronology, and in the material concerning O. Henry assembled chiefly by the energy of the late Harry Peyton Steger are many curious contrasts—little printed rejection slips from Sunday newspapers of an early date keeping company with long and appreciative letters of later date from magazine editors, and clippings from the London *Spectator* comparing O. Henry with Stevenson.

There are letters of O. Henry's telling of his first experiences with "the editor fellers" and recent book reports which show that the public has bought seven hundred and fifty thousand copies of his books in twelve months, and that two of his stories have been put on the stage and many of them dramatized for the "movies."

But in all the material, reports, biographical sketches, and so forth, the most revealing things are his own letters. Almost always they are filled with quaint conceits, usually with a kind of cartoon humour and sometimes with puns. They show little scholarship but much humanity. They are the kind of letters that give the most pleasure to an average person.

In the last years of his life Sydney Porter was never well and he constantly referred to his ill health in his letters, but always with good humour and good cheer.

For instance, he wrote in a letter to his publishers:

My Dear Mr. Lanier:
In a short time, say two weeks at the outside, I'll turn in enough of the book for the purposes you require, as per your recent letter.

LITTLE PICTURES OF O. HENRY

I've been pretty well handicapped for a couple of months and am in the hands of a fine tyrant of a doctor, who makes me come to see him every other day, and who has forbidden me to leave the city until he is through with me, and then only under his own auspices and direction. It seems that the goddess Hygiene and I have been strangers for years; and now Science must step in and repair the damage. My doctor is a miracle worker and promises that in a few weeks he will double my capacity, which sounds very good both for me and for him, when the payment of the bill is considered.

Later he wrote Mr. Steger from Asheville:

DEAR COLONEL STEGER:

I'd have answered your letter, but I've been under the weather with a slight relapse. But on the whole I'm improving vastly. I've a doctor who says I've absolutely no physical trouble except neurasthenia, and that outdoor exercise and air will fix me as good as new. As for the diagnosis of the New York doctors—they are absolutely without foundation. I am twenty pounds lighter and can climb mountains like a goat.

Some time previous to this he wrote in a similar vein to a New York editor:

MY DEAR COLONEL:

I've been intending to write you a long time, but the fact is, I haven't written a line of MS. and scarcely a letter since I've been down here. I've been putting in all my time trying to get back in good shape again. The simple life has been the thing I needed, and by or before Christmas I expect to be at work again in better condition than ever. It is lonesome down here as Broadway when you are broke, but I shall try to stick it out a couple of weeks or so longer.

Tell *Hampton's* not to get discouraged about their story. It'll come pretty soon, and be all the better for the wait. As I said, I haven't sent out a line since I've been here—haven't earned a cent; just lived on nerve and persimmons.

Hope you'll get your project through all right, and make a million. With the same old fraternal and nocturnal regards, I remain,

Yours as usual,

S. P.

His ill health kept him from writing either much or regularly, and consequently he was often temporarily out of money in spite of the fact that his stories were in great demand. To the same editor to whom he wrote of his health at another time he sent this typical letter concerning finances.

The Caledonia.

My Dear Colonel Griffith:

If you've got $100 right in your desk drawer you can have my next story, which will be ready next Tuesday at the latest. That will pay half. The other half on delivery.

I'm always wanting money, and I have to have a century this morning.

I just wanted to give you a chance at the story *at summer rates*, if you want it.

Please give the bearer a positive answer, as I'll have to know at once so as to place it elsewhere this forenoon.

Yours very truly,

Sydney Porter.

P.S.—Story guaranteed satisfactory or another supplied.

This letter was written when his stories were in great demand, when he could sell many more than he could write, and sell them at higher prices than this letter indicates. Not ten years before that, however, he was unknown to the magazine field of literature.

LITTLE PICTURES OF O. HENRY

About the time that he succeeded in selling his first stories to *Everybody's* he began a correspondence with an old friend, A. J. Jennings, ex-train robber, lawyer, author, and reformer, which contains the history of the now famous story Holding Up a Train.* The first letter was as follows:

DEAR JENNINGS

I have intended to write you and Billy every week since I left, but kept postponing it because I expect to move on to Washington (sounds like Stonewall Jackson talk, doesn't it?) almost any time. I am very comfortably situated here, but expect to leave in a couple of weeks anyhow.

I have been doing quite a deal of business with the editors since I got down to work, and have made more than I could at any other business.

. . . . . .

Special regards to "Tex." Love to Hans and Fritz.

Sincerely yours,

W. S. P.

This letter suggested the idea which was later worked out between them, Jennings supplying the data and Porter putting on the finishing touches. In a second letter [included in the Letters already published in "Rolling Stones"] O. Henry explained how the article ought to be written. A part of this letter might well be in every beginner's scrapbook, for there was never better advice about writing: "Begin abruptly without any philosophizing" is part of his doctrine. I know of one magazine office where they

---

* See "Sixes and Sevens."

take out the first paragraph of at least a third of the articles that are accepted for the simple reason that they do not add anything to the story. These first paragraphs bear the same relation to progress in the story as cranking an automobile does to progress on the road. They are merely to get the engine running.

"Describe the facts and details—information is what we want—the main idea is to be natural, direct, and concise." It would be hard to get better advice than this.

In the spirit of these later letters and in their style there is little to distinguish them from the epistles he sent back to North Carolina when he first went to Texas, except the difference in length. This letter to Mrs. Hall, the mother of the men on whose ranch Porter lived, is a fair sample of these early writings.

La Salle Co., Texas.

DEAR MRS. HALL:

Your welcome letter, which I received a good while ago, was much appreciated, and I thought I would answer it in the hopes of getting another from you. I am very short of news, so if you find anything in this letter rather incredible, get Dr. Beall to discount it for you to the proper size. He always questions my veracity since I came out here. Why didn't he do it when I was at home? Dick has got his new house done, and it looks very comfortable and magnificent. It has a tobacco-barn-like grandeur about it that always strikes a stranger with awe, and during a strong north wind the safest place about it is outside at the northern end.

A coloured lady is now slinging hash in the kitchen and has

such an air of command and condescension about her that the pots and kettles all get out of her way with a rush. I think she is a countess or a dukess in disguise. Catulla has grown wonderfully since you left; thirty or forty new houses have gone up and thirty or forty barrels of whiskey gone down. The barkeeper is going to Europe on a tour next summer and is thinking of buying Mexico for his little boy to play with. They are getting along finely with the pasture; there are sixty or seventy men at work on the fence and have been having good weather for working. Ed. Brockman is there in charge of the commissary tent, and issues provisions to the contractors. I saw him last week, and he seemed very well.

Lee came up and asked me to go down to the camps and take Brockman's place for a week or so while he went to San Antonio. Well, I went down some six or seven miles from the ranch. On arriving I counted at the commissary tent nine niggers, sixteen Mexicans, seven hounds, twenty-one six-shooters, four desperadoes, three shotguns, and a barrel of molasses. Inside there were a good many sacks of corn, flour, meal, sugar, beans, coffee, and potatoes, a big box of bacon, some boots, shoes, clothes, saddles, rifles, tobacco, and some more hounds. The work was to issue the stores to the contractors as they sent for them, and was light and easy to do. Out at the rear of the tent they had started a graveyard of men who had either kicked one of the hounds or prophesied a norther. When night came, the gentleman whose good fortune it was to be dispensing the stores gathered up his saddle-blankets, four old corn sacks, an oil coat and a sheep skin, made all the room he could in the tent by shifting and arranging the bacon, meal, etc., gave a sad look at the dogs that immediately filled the vacuum, and went and slept outdoors. The few days I was there I was treated more as a guest than one doomed to labour. Had an offer to gamble from the nigger cook, and was allowed as an especial favour to drive up the nice, pretty horses and give them some corn. And the kind of accommodating old tramps and cowboys that constitute the outfit would drop in and board, and sleep and smoke, and cuss and gamble, and lie and brag, and do everything in their power to make the time pass pleasantly and profitably— to themselves. I enjoyed the thing very much, and one evening when I saw Brockman roll up to the camp, I was very sorry, and went off very early next morning in order to escape the heartbreaking sorrow of parting and leave-taking with the layout.

Now, if you think this fine letter worth a reply, write me a long letter and tell me what I would like to know, and I will rise up and call you a friend in need, and send you a fine cameria obscuria view of this ranch and itemized account of its operations and manifold charms. Tell Dr. Beall not to send me any cake, it would make some postmaster on the road ill if he should eat too much, and I am a friend to all humanity. I am writing by a very poor light, which must excuse bad spelling and uninteresting remarks.

I remain,
Very respectfully yours,
W. S. PORTER.

Everybody well.

More interesting, however, than these early Texas letters in showing the spirit of the man are the letters that he wrote from time to time to his daughter, Margaret, especially those written when she was a little girl. In them he speaks quite often of Uncle Remus, which they evidently read together, and they are all filled with the quaint conceits that enliven the two following:

MY DEAR MARGARET:
I ought to have answered your last letter sooner, but I haven't had a chance. It's getting mighty cool now. It won't be long

before persimmons are ripe in Tennessee. I don't think you ever ate any persimmons, did you? I think persimmons pudden (not pudding) is better than cantalope or watermelon either. If you stay until they get ripe you must get somebody to make you one.

If it snows while you are there, you must try some fried snowballs, too. They are mighty good with Jack Frost gravy.

You must see how big and fat you can get before you go back to Austin.

When I come home I want to find you big and strong enough to pull me all about town on a sled when we have a snow storm. Won't that be nice? I just thought I'd write this little letter in a hurry so the postman would get it, and when I'm in a hurry I never can think of anything to write about. You and Mummy must have a good time, and keep a good lookout and don't let tramps or yellowjackets catch you. I'll try to write something better next time. Write soon.

Your loving

PAPA.

February 14, 1900.

DEAR MARGARET:

It has been quite a long time since I heard from you. I got a letter from you in the last century, and a letter once every hundred years is not very often. I have been waiting from day to day, putting off writing to you, as I have been expecting to have something to send you, but it hasn't come yet, and I thought I would write anyhow.

I hope your watch runs all right. When you write again be sure and look at it and tell me what time it is, so I won't have to get up and look at the clock.

With much love,

PAPA.

As the last of these little sidelights on his character and humour which these letters convey it is fitting to

167

give two showing a peculiarly strong trait—his modesty. He did not seek publicity for himself and he had a lower opinion of his work as work that would last than almost any one else. He wrote in all sincerity to his publishers after the Christmas of 1908:

January 1, 1909.

MY DEAR MR. LANIER:

I want to say how very much I admire and appreciate the splendid edition of my poor stories that you all put in my stocking for Christmas. Unworthy though they were for such a dress, they take on from it such an added importance that I am sure they will stimulate me to do something worthy of such a binding.

I would say by all means don't let the Lipton Pub. Co. escape. Wine 'em or chase 'em in an auto and sell 'em all the "Pancakes" they can eat. Any little drippings of Maple Syrup will come in handy after the havoc of Christmas.

I'll leave things of this sort freely to your judgment.

A Happy New Year to yourself and the House

Very truly yours,

SYDNEY PORTER.

To an admirer who asked for his picture for publication he jocularly refused a request which to most authors is merely a business opportunity. It is a characteristic letter. It was not until very shortly before his death that through much persuasion Sydney Porter finally allowed himself, his picture, and O. Henry to be identified together.

MY DEAR MR. HANNIGAN:

Your letter through McClures' received. Your brief submitted (in re photo) is so flattering that I almost regret being a modest man. I have had none taken for several years except one, which was secured against my wishes and printed by a magazine. I haven't even one in my own possession. I don't believe in inflicting one's picture on the public unless one has done something to justify it—and I never take Peruna.

Sorry! you'd get one if I had it.

That lunch proposition sounds all right—may be in Boston some time and need it.

With regards,

Yours truly,

O. HENRY.

THE KNIGHT IN DISGUISE*

CONCERNING O. HENRY (SYDNEY PORTER)

By Nicholas Vachel Lindsay

IS THIS Sir Philip Sidney, this loud clown,
   The darling of the glad and gaping town?

This is that dubious hero of the press
Whose slangy tongue and insolent address
Were spiced to rouse on Sunday afternoon
The man with yellow journals round him strewn.
We laughed and dozed, then roused and read again
And vowed O. Henry funniest of men.
He always worked a triple-hinged surprise
To end the scene and make one rub his eyes.

He comes with vaudeville, with stare and leer.
He comes with megaphone and specious cheer.
His troup, too fat or short or long or lean,
Step from the pages of the magazine
With slapstick or sombrero or with cane:
The rube, the cowboy, or the masher vain.
They overact each part.   But at the height

---

*This poem is reprinted with one or two slight changes which we make at the author's request, from "General William Booth Enters into Heaven, and Other Poems," by Nicholas Vachel Lindsay, published in 1916 by the Macmillan Company.

THE KNIGHT IN DISGUISE

Of banter and of canter, and delight
The masks fall off for one queer instant there
And show real faces; faces full of care
And desperate longing; love that's hot or cold;
And subtle thoughts, and countenances bold.
The masks go back.   'Tis one more joke.
  Laugh on!
The goodly grown-up company is gone.

No doubt, had he occasion to address
The brilliant court of purple-clad Queen Bess,
He would have wrought for them the best he knew
And led more loftily his actor-crew.
How coolly he misquoted.   'Twas his art—
Slave-scholar, who misquoted—from the heart.
So when we slapped his back with friendly roar
Esop awaited him without the door,—
Esop the Greek, who made dull masters laugh
With little tales of *fox* and *dog* and *calf.*

And be it said, amid his pranks so odd
With something nigh to chivalry he trod—
The fragile drear and driven would defend—
The little shop-girls' knight unto the end.
Yea, he had passed, ere we could understand
The blade of Sidney glimmered in his hand.
Yea, ere we knew, Sir Philip's sword was drawn
With valiant cut and thrust, and he was gone.

THE AMAZING GENIUS OF O. HENRY[*]

By Stephen Leacock

TO BRITISH readers of this book the above heading may look like the title of a comic story of Irish life with the apostrophe gone wrong. It is, alas! only too likely that many, perhaps the majority, of British readers have never heard of O. Henry. It is quite possible also that they are not ashamed of themselves on that account. Such readers would, in truly British fashion, merely classify O. Henry as one of the people that "one has never heard of." If there was any disparagement implied, it would be, as O. Henry himself would have remarked, "on him." And yet there have been sold in the United States, so it is claimed, one million copies of his books.

The point is one which illustrates some of the difficulties which beset the circulation of literature, though written in a common tongue, to and fro across the Atlantic. The British and the American public has each its own preconceived ideas about what it proposes to like. The British reader turns with distaste from anything which bears to him the taint of literary vulgarity or cheapness; he instinctively loves

[*] From "Essays and Literary Studies," 1916, John Lane Co.

172

anything which seems to have the stamp of scholarship and revels in a classical allusion even when he doesn't understand it.

This state of mind has its qualities and its defects. Undoubtedly it makes for the preservation of a standard and a proper appreciation of the literature of the past. It helps to keep the fool in his place, imitating, like a watchful monkey, the admirations of better men. But on its defective side it sins against the light of intellectual honesty.

The attitude of the American reading public is turned the other way. I am not speaking here of the small minority which reads Walter Pater in a soft leather cover, listens to lectures on Bergsonian illusionism and prefers a drama league to a bridge club. I refer to the great mass of the American people, such as live in frame dwellings in the country, or exist in city boarding-houses, ride in the subway, attend a ten-twenty-thirty vaudeville show in preference to an Ibsen drama, and read a one-cent newspaper because it is intellectually easier than a two. This is the real public. It is not, of course, ignorant in the balder sense. A large part of it is, technically, highly educated and absorbs the great mass of the fifty thousand college degrees granted in America each year. But it has an instinctive horror of "learning," such as a cat feels toward running water. It has invented for itself the ominous word "highbrow" as a sign of warning placed over things to be avoided. This word to the American mind conveys much the same "taboo" as haunts the tomb of a Polynesian warrior, or the sacred horror that enveloped in ancient days the dark pine grove of a sylvan deity.

For the ordinary American this word "highbrow" has been pieced together out of recollections of a college professor in a black tail coat and straw hat destroying the peace of an Adirondack boarding-house: out of the unforgotten dullness of a Chautauqua lecture course, or the expiring agonies of a Browning Society. To such a mind the word "highbrow" sweeps a wide and comprehensive area with the red flag of warning. It covers, for example, the whole of history, or, at least, the part of it antecedent to the two last presidential elections. All foreign literature, and all references to it are "highbrow." Shakespeare, except as revived at twenty-five cents a seat with proper alterations in the text, is "highbrow." The works of Milton, the theory of evolution, and, in fact, all science other than Christian science, is "highbrow." A man may only read and discuss such things at his peril. If he does so, he falls forthwith into the class of the Chautauqua lecturer and the vacation professor; he loses all claim to mingle in the main stream of life by taking a hand at ten-cent poker, or giving his views on the outcome of the 1916 elections.

All this, however, by way of preliminary discussion suggested by the strange obscurity of O. Henry in Great Britain, and the wide and increasing popularity of his books in America. O. Henry is, more than any author who ever wrote in the United States, an American writer. As such his work may well appear to a British reader strange and unusual, and, at a casual glance, not attractive. It looks at first sight as if written in American slang, as if it were the careless unrevised production of a journalist. But this is only the impression of an open page, or at best, a judgment formed by a reader who has had the ill-fortune to light upon the less valuable part of O. Henry's output. Let it be remembered that he wrote over two hundred stories. Even in Kentucky, where it is claimed that all whiskey is good whiskey, it is admitted that some whiskey is not so good as the rest. So it may be allowed to the most infatuated admirer of O. Henry, to admit that some of his stories are not as good as the others. Yet even that admission would be reluctant.

But let us recommence in more orthodox fashion.

O. Henry—as he signed himself—was born in 1867, most probably at Greensboro, North Carolina. For the first thirty or thirty-five years of his life, few knew or cared where he was born, or whither he was going. Now that he has been dead five years he shares already with Homer the honour of a disputed birthplace.

His real name was William Sydney Porter. His *nom de plume*, O. Henry—hopelessly tame and colourless from a literary point of view—seems to have been adopted in a whimsical moment, with no great thought as to its aptness. It is amazing that he should have selected so poor a pen name. Those who can remember their first shock of pleased surprise on hearing that Rudyard Kipling's name was really Rudyard Kipling, will feel something like pain in learning that any writer could deliberately christen himself "O. Henry."

The circumstance is all the more peculiar inasmuch as O. Henry's works abound in ingenious nomenclature. The names that he claps on his Central American adventurers are things of joy to the artistic eye—General Perrico Ximenes Villablanca Falcon! Ramon Angel de las Cruzes y Miraflores, president of the republic of Anchuria! Don Señor el Coronel Encarnacion Rios! The very spirit of romance and revolution breathes through them! Or what more beautiful for a Nevada town than Topaz City? What name more appropriate for a commuter's suburb than Floralhurst? And these are only examples among thousands. In all the two hundred stories that O. Henry wrote, there is hardly a single name that is inappropriate or without a proper literary suggestiveness, except the name that he signed to them.

While still a boy, O. Henry (there is no use in calling him anything else) went to Texas, where he worked for three years on a ranch. He drifted into the city of Houston and got employment on a newspaper. A year later he bought a newspaper of his own in Austin, Texas, for the sum of two hundred and fifty dollars. He rechristened it *The Rolling Stone*, wrote it, and even illustrated it, himself. But the paper was too well named. Its editor himself rolled away from it, and from the shores of Texas the wandering restlessness that was characteristic of him wafted him down the great Gulf to the enchanted land of Central America. Here he "knocked around," as he himself has put it, "mostly among refugees and consuls." Here, too, was laid the foundation of much of his most characteristic work—his "Cabbages and Kings," and such stories as Phœbe and The Fourth in Salvador.

Latin America fascinated O. Henry. The languor of the tropics; the sunlit seas with their open bays and broad sanded beaches, with green palms nodding on the slopes above—white-painted steamers lazily at anchor—quaint Spanish towns, with adobe houses and wide squares, sunk in their noon-day sleep—beautiful Señoritas drowsing away the afternoon in hammocks; the tinkling of the mule bells on the mountain track above the town—the cries of unknown birds issuing from the dense green of the unbroken jungle—and at night, in the soft darkness, the low murmur of the guitar, soft thrumming with the voice of love—these are the sights and sounds of O. Henry's Central America. Here live and move his tattered revolutionists, his gaudy generals of the mimic army of the existing republic; hither ply his white-painted steamers of the fruit trade; here the

American consul, with a shadowed past and $600 a year, drinks away the remembrance of his northern energy and his college education in the land of forgetfulness. Hither the absconding banker from the States is dropped from the passing steamer, clutching tight in his shaking hand his valise of stolen dollars; him the disguised detective, lounging beside the little drinking shop, watches with a furtive eye. And here in this land of enchantment the broken lives, the wasted hopes, the ambition that was never reached, the frailty that was never conquered, are somehow pieced together and illuminated into what they might have been—and even the reckless crime and the open sin, viewed in the softened haze of such an atmosphere, are half forgiven.

Whether this is the "real Central America" or not, is of no consequence. It probably is not. The "real Central America" may best be left to the up-to-date specialist, the energetic newspaper expert, or the travelling lady correspondent—to all such persons, in fact, as are capable of writing "Six Weeks in Nicaragua," or "Costa Rica as I Saw It." Most likely the Central America of O. Henry is as gloriously unreal as the London of Charles Dickens, or the Salem of Nathaniel Hawthorne, or any other beautiful picture of the higher truth of life that can be shattered into splinters in the distorting of cold fact.

Form Central America O. Henry rolled, drifted or floated—there was no method in his life—back to Texas again. Here he worked for two weeks in a drugstore. This brief experience supplied him all the rest of his life with local colour and technical material for his stories.* So well has he used it that the obstinate legend still runs that O. Henry was a druggist. A strict examination of his work would show that he knew the names of about seventeen drugs and was able to describe the rolling of pills with the life-like accuracy of one who has rolled them. But it was characteristic of his instinct for literary values that even on this slender basis O. Henry was able to make his characters "take down from shelves" such mysterious things as *Sod. et Pot. Tart.* or discuss whether magnesia carbonate or pulverized glycerine is the best excipient, and in moments of high tragedy poison themselves with "tincture of aconite."

Whether these terms are correctly used or not I do not know. Nor can I conceive that it matters. O. Henry was a literary artist first, last, and always. It was the effect and the feeling that he wanted. For technical accuracy he cared not one whit. There is a certain kind of author who thinks to make literature by introducing, let us say, a plumber using seven different kinds of tap-washers with seven different names; and there is a certain type of reader who is thereby conscious of seven different kinds of ignorance and is fascinated forthwith. From pedantry of this sort O. Henry is entirely free. Even literal accuracy is nothing to him so long as he gets his effect.

---

* As a matter of fact, he did serve as a drug clerk for a considerable period of time, when a very young man, in his uncle's drugstore in Greensboro.—ED.

Thus he commences one of his stories with the brazen
statement: "In Texas you may journey for a thousand miles in a straight line." You can't, of course;
and O. Henry knew it. It is only his way of saying
that Texas is a very big place. So with his tincture
of aconite. It may be poisonous or it may not be.
But it sounds poisonous and that is enough for O.
Henry. This is true art.

After his brief drugstore experience O. Henry
moved to New Orleans. Even in his Texan and
Central American days he seems to have scribbled
stories. In New Orleans he set to work deliberately
as a writer. Much of his best work was poured
forth with prodigality of genius into the columns of
the daily press without thought or fame. The
money that he received, so it is said, was but a pit-
tance. Stories that would sell to-day—were O.
Henry alive and writing them now—for a thousand
dollars, went for next to nothing. Throughout his
life money meant little or nothing to him. If he had
it, he spent it, loaned it, or gave it away. When he
had it not he bargained with an editor for the payment in advance of a story which he meant to write,
and of which he exhibited the title or a few sentences
as a sample, and which he wrote, faithfully enough,
"when he got round to it." The story runs of how
one night a beggar on the street asked O. Henry
for money. He drew forth a coin from his pocket in
the darkness and handed it to the man. A few mo-

ments later the beggar looked at the coin under a street lamp, and, being even such a beggar as O. Henry loved to write about, he came running back with the words, "Say, you made a mistake, this is a twenty-dollar gold piece." "I know it is," said O. Henry, "but it's all I have."

The story may not be true. But at least it ought to be.

From New Orleans O. Henry moved to New York and became, for the rest of his life, a unit among the "four million" dwellers in flats and apartment houses and sand-stone palaces who live within the roar of the elevated railway, and from whom the pale light of the moon and the small effects of the planetary system are overwhelmed in the glare of the Great White Way. Here O. Henry's finest work was done— inimitable, unsurpassable stories that make up the volumes entitled "The Four Million," "The Trimmed Lamp," and "The Voice of the City."

Marvellous indeed they are. Written offhand with the bold carelessness of the pen that only genius dare use, but revealing behind them such a glow of the imagination and such a depth of understanding of the human heart as only genius can make manifest.

What O. Henry did for Central America he does again for New York. It is transformed by the magic of his imagination. He waves a wand over it and it becomes a city of mystery and romance. It is no longer the roaring, surging metropolis that we thought we knew, with its clattering elevated, its

unending crowds, and on every side the repellent
selfishness of the rich, the grim struggle of the poor,
and the listless despair of the outcast. It has become, as O. Henry loves to call it, Bagdad upon the
Subway. The glare has gone. There is a soft light
suffusing the city. Its corner drugstores turn to
enchanted bazaars. From the open doors of its
restaurants and palm rooms there issues such a melody of softened music that we feel we have but to
cross the threshold and there is Bagdad waiting for
us beyond. A transformed waiter hands us to a
chair at a little table—Arabian, I will swear it—
beside an enchanted rubber tree. There is red wine
such as Omar Khayyam drank, here on Sixth Avenue.
At the tables about us are a strange and interesting
crew—dervishes in the disguise of American business
men, caliphs masquerading as tourists, bedouins from
Syria, and fierce fantassins from the desert turned into
western visitors from Texas, and among them—can
we believe our eyes—houris from the inner harems of
Ispahan and Candahar, whom we mistook but yesterday for the ladies of a Shubert chorus! As we pass
out we pay our money to an enchanted cashier with
golden hair—sitting behind glass—under the spell of
some magician without a doubt, and then taking O.
Henry's hand we wander forth among the ever-
changing scenes of night adventure, the mingled
tragedy and humour of The Four Million that his pen
alone can depict. Nor did ever Haroun-al-Rashid
and his viziers, wandering at will in the narrow streets

of their Arabian city, meet such varied adventure as lies before us, strolling hand in hand with O. Henry in the new Bagdad that he reveals.

But let us turn to the stories themselves. O. Henry wrote in all two hundred short stories of an average of about fifteen pages each. This was the form in which his literary activity shaped itself by instinct. A novel he never wrote, a play he often meditated but never achieved. One of his books— "Cabbages and Kings"—can make a certain claim to be continuous. But even this is rather a collection of little stories than a single piece of fiction. But it is an error of the grossest kind to say that O. Henry's work is not sustained. In reality his canvas is vast. His New York stories, like those of Central America or of the West, form one great picture as gloriously comprehensive in its scope as the lengthiest novels of a Dickens or the canvas of a Da Vinci. It is only the method that is different, not the result.

It is hard indeed to illustrate O. Henry's genius by the quotation of single phrases and sentences. The humour that is in his work lies too deep for that. His is not the comic wit that explodes the reader into a huge guffaw of laughter and vanishes. His humour is of that deep quality that smiles at life itself and mingles our amusement with our tears.

Still harder is it to try to show the amazing genius of O. Henry as a "plot maker," as a designer of incident. No one better than he can hold the reader in suspense. Nay, more than that, the reader scarcely knows that he is "suspended," until at the very close of the story O. Henry, so to speak, turns on the lights and the whole tale is revealed as an entirety. But to do justice to a plot in a few paragraphs is almost impossible. Let the reader consider to what a few poor shreds even the best of our novels or plays is reduced, when we try to set forth the basis of it in the condensed phrase of a text-book of literature, or diminish it to the language of the "scenario" of a moving picture. Let us take an example.

We will transcribe our immortal "Hamlet" as faithfully as we can into a few words with an eye to explain the plot and nothing else. It will run about as follows:

"Hamlet's uncle kills his father and marries his mother, and Hamlet is so disturbed about this that he either is mad or pretends to be mad. In this condition he drives his sweetheart insane and she drowns, or practically drowns, herself. Hamlet then kills his uncle's chief adviser behind an arras either in mistake for a rat, or not. Hamlet then gives poison to his uncle and his mother, stabs Laertes and kills himself. There is much discussion among the critics as to whether his actions justify us in calling him insane."

There! The example is, perhaps, not altogether convincing. It does not seem somehow, faithful though it is, to do Shakespeare justice. But let it at least illustrate the point under discussion. The mere bones of a plot are nothing. We could scarcely form a judgment on female beauty by studying the skeletons of a museum of anatomy.

But with this distinct understanding, let me try to present the outline of a typical O. Henry story. I select it from the volume entitled "The Gentle Grafter," a book that is mainly concerned with the wiles of Jeff Peters and his partners and associates. Mr. Peters, who acts as the narrator of most of the stories, typifies the perennial fakir and itinerant grafter of the Western States—ready to turn his hand to anything from selling patent medicines under a naphtha lamp on the street corner of a Western town to peddling bargain Bibles from farm to farm—anything, in short, that does not involve work and carries with it the peculiar excitement of trying to keep out of the State penitentiary. All the world loves a grafter—at least a genial and ingenious grafter—a Robin Hood who plunders an abbot to feed a beggar, an Alfred Jingle, a Scapin, a Raffles, or any of the multifarious characters of the world's literature who reveal the fact that much that is best in humanity may flourish even on the shadowy side of technical iniquity. Of this glorious company is Mr. Jefferson Peters. But let us take him as he is revealed in "Jeff Peters as a Personal Magnet" and let us allow him to introduce himself and his business.

"I struck Fisher Hill," Mr. Peters relates, "in a buckskin suit, moccasins, long hair, and a thirty-carat diamond ring that I got from an actor in Texarkana.

I don't know what he ever did with the pocket-knife I swapped him for it.

"I was Dr. Waugh-hoo, the celebrated Indian medicine man. I carried only one best bet just then, and that was Resurrection Bitters. It was made of life-giving plants and herbs accidentally discovered by Ta-qua-la, the beautiful wife of the chief of the Choctaw Nation, while gathering truck to garnish a platter of boiled dog for an annual corn dance. . . ." In the capacity of Dr. Waugh-hoo, Mr. Peters "struck Fisher Hill." He went to a druggist and got credit for half a gross of eight-ounce bottles and corks, and with the help of the running water from the tap in the hotel room, he spent a long evening manufacturing Resurrection Bitter . The next evening the sales began. The bitters at fifty cents a bottle "started off like sweetbreads on toast at a vegetarian dinner." Then there intervenes a constable with a German silver badge. "Have you got a city license?" he asks, and Mr. Peters's medicinal activity comes to a full stop. The threat of prosecution under the law for practising medicine without a license puts Mr. Peters for the moment out of business.

He returns sadly to his hotel, pondering on his next move. Here by good fortune he meets a former acquaintance, a certain Andy Tucker, who has just finished a tour in the Southern States, working the Great Cupid Combination Package on the chivalrous and unsuspecting South.

"Andy," says Jeff, in speaking of his friend's

credentials, "was a good street man: and he was more than that—he respected his profession and was satisfied with 300 per cent. profit. He had plenty of offers to go into the illegitimate drug and garden seed business, but he was never to be tempted off the straight path."

Andy and Jeff take counsel together in long debate on the porch of the hotel.

And here, apparently, a piece of good luck came to Jeff's help. The very next morning a messenger brings word that the Mayor of the town is suddenly taken ill. The only doctor of the place is twenty miles away. Jeff Peters is summoned to the Mayor's bedside. . . . "This Mayor Banks," Jeff relates, "was in bed all but his whiskers and feet. He was making internal noises that would have had everybody in San Francisco hiking for the parks. A young man was standing by the bedside holding a cup of water. . . ." Mr. Peters, called to the patient's side, is very cautious. He draws attention to the fact that he is not a qualified practitioner, is not "a regular disciple of S. Q. Lapius."

The Mayor groans in pain. The young man at the bedside, introduced as Mr. Biddle, the Mayor's nephew, urges Mr. Peters—or Doctor Waugh-hoo— in the name of common humanity to attempt a cure.

Finally Jeff Peters promises to treat the Mayor by "scientific demonstration." He proposes, he says, to make use of the "great doctrine of psychic financiering—of the enlightening school of long-distance

187

subconscious treatment of fallacies and meningitis—
of that wonderful indoor sport known as personal
magnetism." But he warns the Mayor that the
treatment is difficult. It uses up great quantities of
soul strength. It comes high. It cannot be attempted under two hundred and fifty dollars.

The Mayor groans. But he yields. The treatment begins.

"You ain't sick," says Dr. Waugh-hoo, looking the
patient right in the eye. "You ain't got any pain.
The right lobe of your perihelion is subsided."

The result is surprising. The Mayor's system
seems to respond at once. "I do feel some better,
Doc," he says, "darned if I don't."

Mr. Peters assumes a triumphant air. He promises
to return next day for a second and final treatment.

"I'll come back," he says to the young man, "at
eleven. You may give him eight drops of turpentine
and three pounds of steak. Good-morning."

Next day the final treatment is given. The Mayor
is completely restored. Two hundred and fifty dollars, all in cash, is handed to "Dr. Waugh-hoo." The
young man asks for a receipt. It is no sooner written
out by Jeff Peters, than:

"'Now do your duty, officer,' says the Mayor,
grinning much unlike a sick man.

"Mr. Biddle lays his hand on my arm.

"'You're under arrest, Dr. Waugh-hoo, alias
Peters,' says he, 'for practising medicine without
authority under the State law.'

"'Who are you?' I asks.

"'I'll tell you who he is,' says Mr. Mayor, sitting up in bed. 'He's a detective employed by the State Medical Society. He's been following you over five counties. He came to me yesterday and we fixed up this scheme to catch you. I guess you won't do any more doctoring around these parts, Mr. Fakir. What was it you said I had, Doc?' the Mayor laughs, 'compound—well, it wasn't softening of the brain, I guess, anyway.'"

Ingenious, isn't it? One hadn't suspected it. But let the reader kindly note the conclusion of the story as it follows, handled with the lightning rapidity of a conjuring trick.

"'Come on, officer,' says I, dignified. 'I may as well make the best of it.' And then I turns to old Banks and rattles my chains.

"'Mr. Mayor,' says I, 'the time will come soon when you'll believe that personal magnetism is a success. And you'll be sure that it succeeded in this case, too.'

"And I guess it did.

"When we got nearly to the gate, I says: 'We might meet somebody now, Andy. I reckon you better take 'em off, and——' Hey? Why, of course it was Andy Tucker. That was his scheme; and that's how we got the capital to go into business together."

Now let us set beside this a story of a different type, The Furnished Room, which appears in the volume called "The Four Million." It shows O. Henry at his best as a master of that supreme pathos that springs, with but little adventitious aid of time or circumstance, from the fundamental things of life itself. In the sheer art of narration there is nothing done by Maupassant that surpasses The Furnished Room. The story runs—so far as one dare attempt to reproduce it without quoting it all word for word —after this fashion.

The scene is laid in New York in the lost district of the lower West Side, where the wandering feet of actors and one-week transients seek furnished rooms in dilapidated houses of fallen grandeur.

One evening after dark a young man prowled among these crumbling red mansions, ringing their bells. At the twelfth he rested his lean hand-baggage upon the step and wiped the dust from his hatband and forehead. The bell sounded faint and far away in some remote hollow depths. . . . "I have the third floor back vacant since a week back," says the landlady. . . . "It's a nice room. It ain't often vacant. I had some most elegant people in it last summer—no trouble at all and paid in advance to the minute. The water's at the end of the hall. Sprowls and Mooney kept it three months. They done a vaudeville sketch. Miss B'retta Sprowls, you may have heard of her—Oh, that was just the stage name—right there over the dresser is where the marriage certificate hung, framed. The gas is here and you see there's plenty of closet room. It's a room every one likes. It never stays idle long——"

The young man takes the room, paying a week in advance. Then he asks:

"A young girl—Miss Vashner—Miss Eloise Vashner—do you remember such a one among your lodgers? She would be singing on the stage most likely."

The landlady shakes her head. They comes and goes, she tells him, she doesn't call that one to mind.

It is the same answer that he has been receiving, up and down, in the crumbling houses of the lost district, through weeks and months of wandering. No, always no. Five months of ceaseless interrogation and the inevitable negative. So much time spent by day in questioning managers, agents, schools, and choruses; by night among the audiences of theatres from all-star casts down to music halls so low that he dreaded to find what he most hoped for. . . . The young man, left in his sordid room of the third floor back, among its decayed furniture, its ragged brocade upholstery, sinks into a chair. The dead weight of despair is on him. . . . Then, suddenly, as he rested there, the room was filled with the strong, sweet odour of mignonette—the flower that she had always loved, the perfume that she had always worn. It is as if her very presence was beside him in the empty room. He rises. He cries aloud,

191

"What, dear?" as if she had called to him. She has been there in the room. He knows it. He feels it. Then eager, tremulous with hope, he searches the room, tears open the crazy chest of drawers, fumbles upon the shelves, for some sign of her. Nothing and still nothing—a crumpled playbill, a half-smoked cigar, the dreary and ignoble small records of many a peripatetic tenant, but of the woman that he seeks, nothing. Yet still that haunting perfume that seems to speak her presence at his very side.

The young man dashes trembling from the room. Again he questions the landlady—was there not, before him in the room, a young lady? Surely there must have been—fair, of medium height, and with reddish gold hair? Surely there was?

But the landlady, as if obdurate, shakes her head. "I can tell you again," she says, "'twas Sprowls and Mooney, as I said. Miss B'retta Sprowls, it was, in the theatres, but Missis Mooney she was. The marriage certificate hung, framed, on a nail over——"

. . . . The young man returns to his room. It is all over. His search in vain. The ebbing of his last hope has drained his faith. . . . For a time he sat staring at the yellow, singing gaslight. Then he rose. He walked to the bed and began to tear the sheets into strips. With the blade of his knife he drove them tightly into every crevice around windows and door. When all was snug and taut he turned out the light, turned the gas full on again, and laid himself gratefully upon the bed.

And now let the reader note the ending paragraphs of the story, so told that not one word of it must be altered or abridged from the form in which O. Henry framed it.

It was Mrs. McCool's night to go with the can for beer. So she fetched it and sat with Mrs. Purdy (the landlady) in one of those subterranean retreats where housekeepers foregather and the worm dieth seldom.

"I rented out my third floor, back, this evening," said Mrs. Purdy, across a fine circle of foam. "A young man took it. He went up to bed two hours ago."

"Now, did ye, Mrs. Purdy, ma'am?" said Mrs. McCool with intense admiration. "You do be a wonder for rentin' rooms of that kind. And did ye tell him, then?" she concluded in a husky whisper laden with mystery.

"Rooms," said Mrs. Purdy, in her furriest tones, "are furnished for to rent. I did not tell him, Mrs. McCool."

"'Tis right ye are, ma'am; 'tis by renting rooms we kape alive. Ye have the rale sense for business, ma'am. There be many people will rayjict the rentin' of a room if they be tould a suicide has been after dyin' in the bed of it."

"As you say, we has our living to be making," remarked Mrs. Purdy.

"Yis, ma'am; 'tis true. 'Tis just one wake ago

this day I helped ye lay out the third floor, back. A pretty slip of a colleen she was to be killin' herself wid the gas—a swate little face she had, Mrs. Purdy, ma'am."

"She'd a-been called handsome, as you say,' said Mrs. Purdy, assenting but critical, "but for that mole she had a-growin' by her left eyebrow. Do fill up your glass again, Mrs. McCool."

Beyond these two stories I do not care to go. But if the reader is not satisfied let him procure for himself the story called A Municipal Report in the volume "Strictly Business." After he has read it he will either pronounce O. Henry one of the greatest masters of modern fiction or else—well, or else he is a jackass. Let us put it that way.

O. Henry lived some nine years in New York but little known to the public at large. Toward the end there came to him success, a competence, and something that might be called celebrity if not fame. But it was marvellous how his light remained hid. The time came when the best known magazines eagerly sought his work. He could have commanded his own price. But the notoriety of noisy success, the personal triumph of literary conspicuousness he neither achieved nor envied. A certain cruel experience of his earlier days—tragic, unmerited, and not here to be recorded—had left him shy of mankind at large and, in the personal sense, anxious only for obscurity. Even when the American public in tens and hundreds of thousands read his matchless stories, they read them, so to speak, in isolated fashion, as personal discoveries, unaware for years of the collective greatness of O. Henry's work viewed as a total. The few who were privileged to know him seem to have valued him beyond all others and to have found him even greater than his work. And then, in mid-career as it seemed, there was laid upon him the hand of a wasting and mortal disease, which brought him slowly to his end, his courage and his gentle kindliness unbroken to the last. "I shall die," he said one winter with one of the quoted phrases that fell so aptly from his lips, "in the good old summer time." And "in the good old summer time" with a smile and a jest upon his lips he died. "Don't turn down the light," he is reported to have said to those beside his bed, and then, as the words of a popular song flickered across his mind, he added, "I'm afraid to go home in the dark."

That was in the summer of 1910. Since his death, his fame in America has grown greater and greater with every year. The laurel wreath that should have crowned his brow is exchanged for the garland laid upon his grave. And the time is coming, let us hope, when the whole English-speaking world will recognize in O. Henry one of the great masters of modern literature.

O. HENRY: AN ENGLISH VIEW

By A. St. John Adcock

USUALLY, when we write of how the critics and the public of an earlier generation were slow to recognize the genius of Meredith or Mark Rutherford, we do it with an air of severe self-righteousness which covers an implication that we in our more enlightened age are not likely to repeat such blunders, that the general taste and critical acumen of our time may safely be relied upon to assess contemporary authors at their true value and put them, with unerring promptitude, into their proper places. The fact is, of course, that even our modern literary judgments are not infallible, and that we are really in no position at all to throw stones at our forefathers. It were sufficient for us if we devoted our energies to getting the beam out of our own eye and left the dead past to bury its dead mistakes.

Take the very modern instance of O. Henry. Thousands of us are reading his stories at present and realizing with astonishment that he was a great literary artist—with astonishment because, though we are only just arriving at this knowledge of him, we learn that he commenced to write before the end of last century, and has been five years dead. Even in America, where he belonged, recognition came to him slowly; it was only toward the close of his life that he began to be counted as anything more than a popular magazine author; but now, in the States, they have sold more than a million copies of his books. His publishers announce in their advertisements that "up goes the sale of O. Henry, higher and higher every day," that he has "beaten the world record for the sale of short stories"; and the critics compete with each other in comparing him to Poe and Bret Harte, to Mark Twain and Dickens, to de Maupassant and Kipling. We cannot put ourselves right by saying that he was an American, for in the last few years at least two attempts have been made to introduce him to English readers, and both of them failed. Then a little while ago Mr. Eveleigh Nash embarked on a third attempt and commenced the publication of a uniform edition of the works of O. Henry in twelve three-and-sixpenny volumes. They hung fire a little at first, I believe, but by degrees made headway, and before the series was completed it had achieved a large and increasing success. This was recently followed by an announcement of the issue of the twelve volumes in a shilling edition by Messrs. Hodder & Stoughton; the first six have appeared, and the remainder are to be published before the end of the year, and as the publishers estimate that by then, at the present rate of sale, at least half a million copies will have been sold, one may take it that, at long last, O. Henry is triumphantly entering into his kingdom.

In a brilliant appreciation of The Amazing Genius of O. Henry,* in his new book, "Essays and Literary Studies" (John Lane), Professor Stephen Leacock speaks of the wide and increasing popularity of O. Henry in America, and of his "strange obscurity" in Great Britain. He thinks it "only too likely that many, perhaps the majority, of British readers have never heard of O. Henry." That was certainly true when it was written, but in the last six months our long-suffering public has risen above the reproach. Professor Leacock tries to suggest a reason for our indifference. "The British reader turns with distaste," he says, "from anything which bears to him the taint of literary vulgarity or cheapness; he instinctively loves anything which seems to have the stamp of scholarship, and revels in a classical allusion even when he doesn't understand it." But for the sting in its tail and the passage that succeeds it, I should suspect this sentence of irony, for the British reader received at once and with open arms the joyous extravagances of Max Adeler (who, by the way, should not have been entirely ignored in Professor Leacock's essay on "American Humour"), and there is nothing in "Elbow Room" or "Out of the Hurly-Burly" that is funnier or more quaintly humorous than some of Henry's stories. But O. Henry can move you to tears as

* Reprinted in this volume, pp. 172-195.

well as to laughter—you have not finished with him
when you have called him a humourist. He has all
the gifts of the supreme teller of tales, is master of
tragedy as well as of burlesque, of comedy and of
romance, of the domestic and the mystery-tale of
common life, and has a delicate skill in stories of the
supernatural. Through every change of his theme
runs a broad, genial understanding of all sorts of
humanity, and his familiar, sometimes casually conversational style conceals a finished narrative art that
amply justifies Professor Leacock in naming him
"one of the great masters of modern literature." He
is not, then, of that cheap type of author from whom,
as the Professor says, the British reader "turns with
distaste." He has not been received among us sooner
simply because, to repeat Mr. Leacock's statement,
"the majority of British readers have never heard of
O. Henry," and obviously until they have heard of
him it is impossible that they should read him.
Therefore, the blame for our not sooner appreciating
him rests, not on our general public, but on our critics
and publishers. If he had been adequately published,
and adequately reviewed over here before, British
readers must have heard of him, and their complete
vindication lies in the fact that now, when at length
he has been adequately published and reviewed and
so brought to their notice, they are reading his books
as fast as they can lay hands on them. . . .

The life he lived was the life that was best for him.
Every phase of it had its share in making him the

prose troubadour that he became. Half his books are filled with stories that are shaped and coloured by his roamings, and the other half with stories that he gathered in the busy ways and, particularly, in the byways of—"Little Old New York." For the scenes, incidents, and characters of his tales he had not need to travel far outside the range of his own experiences, and it is probably this that helps to give them the carelessly intimate air of reality that is part of their strength. He touches in his descriptions lightly and swiftly, yet whether he is telling of the old-world quaintness of North Carolina, the rough law-lessness of Texas, the strange glamour of New Or-leans, the slumberous, bizarre charm of obscure South American coast towns, or the noise and bustle and squalour and up-to-date magnificence of New York, his stories are steeped in colour and atmosphere. You come to think of his men and women less as characters he has drawn than as people he has known, he writes of them with such familiar acquaintance, and makes them so vividly actual to you. He is as sure and as cunning in the presentment of his exquisite señoritas, his faded, dignified Spanish grandees and planters and traders and picturesque rather comic-opera Presidents of small South American republics, as in drawing his wonderful gallery of Bowery boys, financiers, clerks, shop-girls, workers, and New York aristocrats. You scarcely realize them as creations, they seem to walk into his pages without effort. His women are, at least, as varied in type and as intensely human as his men: he wins your sympathy for Isabel Guilbert,* who was "Eve after the fall but before the bitterness of it was felt," who "wore life as a rose in her bosom," and who, according to Keogh, could "look at a man once, and he'll turn monkey and climb trees to pick cocoanuts for her," no less than he wins it for Norah, the self-sacrificing little sewing-girl, of Blind Man's Holiday,† or the practical, loyally passionate wife, Santa Yeager, of Hearts and Crosses,‡ or the delightful Mrs. Cassidy who accepts the blows of her drunken husband as proof of his love ("Who else has got a right to be beat? I'd just like to catch him once beating anybody else!") in A Harlem Tragedy,§ which would be grotesquely farcical if it were not for its droll air of truth and the curious sense of pathos that underlies it. . . .

I am not going to attempt to say which is the best of his tales; they vary so widely in subject and manner that it is impossible to compare them. There were moods in which he saw New York in all its solid, material, commonplace realism, and moods in which it became to him "Bagdad-on-the-Subway," and was full of romance, as Soho is in Stevenson's "New Arabian Nights." His Wild West stories are a subtle blend of humour, pathos, and picturesqueness; some of his town and country stories delight you by their

* See "Cabbages and Kings."
† See "Whirligigs."
‡ See "Heart of the West."
§ See "The Trimmed Lamp."

homely naturalness, others are alive with sensation and excitement, others again are pure fantasy or things for nothing but laughter. Then there are such as "Roads of Destiny," which, with a strange dream-like quality, a haunting, imaginative suggestiveness, unfolds three stories of the same man—as one might see them in prevision—showing that whichever way of life he had chosen he would have been brought to the same appointed end. The eerie touch of other-world influences is upon you in this, as it is in The Door of Unrest,* an uncanny, queerly humorous legend of the Wandering Jew in a modern American city; and as it is in The Furnished Room,† which Professor Leacock justly singles out as one of the finest of O. Henry's works. "It shows O. Henry at his best," he says, "as a master of that supreme pathos that springs, with but little adventitious aid of time or circumstance, from the fundamental things of life itself. In the sheer art of narration there is nothing done by Maupassant that surpasses The Furnished Room." It could only be misrepresented in a summary, for though O. Henry always has a good story to tell, its effectiveness is always heightened immeasurably by his manner of telling it.

It is in sheer art of narration, and in the breadth and depth of his knowledge of humanity and his sympathy with it that he chiefly excels. He was too big a man to be nothing but an artist, and the bigger

* See "Sixes and Sevens."
† See "The Four Million."

artist for that reason. He has none of the conscious stylist's elaborate little tricks with words, for he is a master of language and not its slave. He is as happily colloquial as Kipling was in his early tales, but his style is as individual, as naturally his own, as a man's voice may be. He seems to go as he pleases, writing apparently just whatever words happen to be in the ink, yet all the while he is getting hold of his reader's interest, subtly shaping his narrative with the storyteller's unerring instinct, generally allowing you no glimpse of its culminating point until you are right on it. "The art of narrative," said Keogh, in "Cabbages and Kings," "consists in concealing from your audience everything it wants to know until after you expose your favourite opinions on topics foreign to the subject. A good story is like a bitter pill with the sugar coating inside of it"; and this art O. Henry practises with a skill that is invariably admirable and at times startling. More than once he leads you deftly on till you arrive at what would seem an ingenious ending, then in a sudden paragraph he will give the whole thing a quick turn and land you in a still more ingenious climax that leaves victory in the hands of the character who had seemed to have lost.

"Cabbages and Kings," a series of stories held together by a central thread of interest, is the nearest O. Henry came to writing a novel. Toward the end of his career his publishers urged h'm to write one and among his papers after his death was found an unfinished reply to them setting out something of his idea of the novel he would like to attempt. It was to be the story of an individual, not of a type—"the *true* record of a man's thoughts, his descriptions of his mischances and adventures, his *true* opinions of life as he has seen it, and his *absolutely honest* deductions, comments, and views upon the different phases of life he passes through." It was not to be autobiography: "most autobiographies are insincere from beginning to end. About the only chance for the truth to be told is in fiction."

But his novel remains without a title in the list of unwritten books. Whether, if it had been written, it would have proved him as great an artist on the larger canvas as he is on the smaller, is a vain speculation and a matter of no moment. What matters is that in these twelve volumes of his he has done enough to add much and permanently to the world's sources of pleasure, and enough to give him an assured place among the masters of modern fiction.

THE MISADVENTURES IN MUSICAL COMEDY OF O. HENRY AND FRANKLIN P. ADAMS*

A CHICAGO manager started the trouble. He wrote as follows to Mr. Adams:

I am very anxious to secure a piece on the lines of "The Time, the Place, and the Girl." I say that for the reason that I have a star who is really a sensation, and we want to get him a piece that will suit him. It must be a modern character as he is a nice-looking fellow and I believe in a man continuing in a character in which he has achieved success. He is quite a fast talker, natty, dances very well, and sings excellently and is in every way very clever. We will have an opportunity to do a piece here by April and my ambition now is to get a play for him.

O. Henry has written a story for *Collier's* that fits Y——to the ground. How would you like to coöperate with him?

The foregoing letter was received February 10, 1909. Mr. Adams welcomed the opportunity it presented, and took kindly to the idea of collaborating with O. Henry.

He says: "I called on O. Henry and we discussed it at length. His other pseudonym was Barkis. We

* Adapted from "Lo, the Poor Musical Comedy," by Franklin P. Adams, published in *The Success Magazine*, October, 1910.

agreed to collaborate, both of us to work on the dialogue and both on the lyrics. And as it happened it was almost a complete collaboration. Hardly an independent line was written. . . .

"We were interested in the piece and anxious to please the manager who had gone out of his way to get us. . . . O. Henry and I would convene nearly every afternoon and talk the thing over, outlining scenes, making notes of lines of dialogue, tentative ideas for lyrics, etc. . . . We enjoyed working at this time. It was fun blocking out the plans and O. Henry was simply shedding whimsical ideas for lines and situations."

The plot concerned an anthropological expedition to Yucatan to inquire into the theory that the American Indian was descended from the ancient Aztecs. O. Henry called this *aztechnology* and "The Enthusiaztecs" was at first suggested for the title; but the manager would have none of it—was pleased to say that it sounded like the title of an amateur performance given by the Lincoln Memorial High School, and even went so far as to accuse the librettists of offences smacking not a little of the crime of highbrowism.

However, "The title inspiration soon came," says Mr. Adams. "It was O. Henry's and I am still of the opinion that it was an excellent title—'Lo.' As originally written the comedy emphasized the reversion to type of the Indian, and tried to show, as Pope suggested, after

'Lo, the poor Indian! whose untutored mind
Sees God in clouds, or hears him in the wind. . . .'

that

'To be, contents his natural desire.
He asks no angel's wing, no seraph's fire.'"

The manager accepted this title with enthusiasm, for "You can advertise it easy and it looks good in type."

They had supposed that in the construction of a musical comedy the librettist first wrote some verses and the composer then evolved a melody to fit them. "But," Mr. Adams states, "most of our songs were constructed to fit tunes the composer had already written. I am not saying that this method is absolutely wrong, but it is infinitely harder work for the lyricist. Take an unfamiliar melody—often irregular as to meter—and try to fit intelligible, singable, rhythmical words to it. No wonder that after a month or two of it the barber tells you that it's getting pretty thin on top."

Difficulties and disagreements with the manager now came thick and fast: "'Two and two,' says the manager, profoundly and confidentially, 'are five.' 'But'—you begin. 'You're inexperienced,' says the manager, 'and you don't know; *believe me*. I've been in this business twenty-seven years. We need comedy here. Laughs is what we want, all the time.'"

The infallible manager became convinced of the hopelessness of their ignorance of practical theatrical exigencies. "The second act was bad, the first scene was an interior," etc., etc. He engaged another man to rewrite the book. This was done. The manager approved the new man's outline. But his dialogue was rejected wholly, and the original collaborators had more rewriting to do. O. Henry never worked harder or more conscientiously on anything in his life. He lost weight. He worried. Day and night they worked on the comedy. Again they sent on the completed script, this being the third or fourth "rewrite." As they mailed it, O. Henry recited in a singular minor key:

> "Dramatization is vexation;
> Revision is as bad;
> This comedy perplexes me
> And managers drive me mad!"

Followed more dissatisfaction on the manager's part, and several harassing trips to Chicago.

But, finally, "Lo" was produced. Mr. Adams tells the tale: "The first performance was given in Aurora, Illinois, on August 25, 1909. With two exceptions—any members of the company who chance to read this will wonder who the second one I have in mind is—the acting was mediocre. But it 'went' well and the unbiassed Auroran seemed to like it. I rather enjoyed it myself. There was no Night of Triumph, however. After the performance the manager met me on the street. 'Come to my room before you go to bed,' he said. 'Got to fix up that second act. It's rotten. . . . So I did some more rewriting, which I think was never even tried out. I never heard of it, at any rate.

"After performances in Waukegan, Illinois, and Janesville, Wisconsin, 'Lo' opened in Milwaukee for a week's engagement. It seemed to please; the newspapers 'treated us lovely,' as the management had it.

"But at the age of fourteen weeks it breathed its last, on December 5th, in St. Joseph, Missouri. Its parents, bearing up nobly, learned the sad news through a stray newspaper paragraph. . . .

"That is the plain, unjapalacked story. I'm not recriminating. Taking one consideration with another, however, the librettist's lot is not a snappy one."

What Mr. Adams calls "Lo, the Poor Musical Comedy," is dead and gone, and no man knoweth the place of its sepulture. But most of the lyrics have survived.

Mr. Adams tells us that his collaboration with O. Henry was unusually thoroughgoing—hardly an independent line was written. But "Snap Shots" was all O. Henry's.

SNAP SHOTS

Watch out, lovers, when you promenade;
When you kiss and coo, in the deep moon shade.
When you're close together in the grape-vine swing,

When you are a-courting or philandering.
Mabel, Maud and Ann, Nellie, May and Fan,
Keep your eyes open for the Snap Shot Man!

Snap! Shots! Hear the shutter close!
What a world of roguishness the little snapper shows!
Click! Click! Caught you unaware—
Snap Shot Man'll get you if you don't take care!

Watch out, you, Sir, when your wife's away,
When you take your "cousin" to see the play,
With best aisle seats, and in the bass drum row,
And holding her hand when all the lights are low.
Billy, Bob and Dan, Smith and Harrigan,
Keep your eyes open for the Snap Shot Man!

Snap! Shots! Hear the snapper snap!
Got you just as safe as any squirrel in a trap.
Click! Click! Got you just as slick—
Cam'ra man'll snap you if you don't be quick!

When you're swimming in your bathing suit,
And Hubby's in town, slaving like a brute,
And handsome young stranger, "Teach you how to swim?"
It's not my affair, it's up to you and him.
But, Adele and Pearl, in the water's swirl,
Keep your eyes open for the Snap Shot Girl.

Snap! Shots! Just a button pressed—
Only seems a trifle, but the courts'll do the rest.
Click! Click! Caught you P. Q. D.
Snap Shot Girl'll get you if you trifle in the sea.

In Yucatan, of course owes its inspiration to O.
Henry's sojourn in the exiles' haven, Honduras. But

its lyrical tone is so strong, the farcical so nearly
absent, that one guesses it to be mainly from the pen
of Mr. Adams.

IN YUCATAN

In a *dolce far niente*
Mood amid the fruits and flowers,
Ladies in a land of plenty
Idly watch the ebbing hours;
In this paradise Utopian
Time and tide are cornucopian;
So we say *"Festina lente,"*
All the sands of time are ours.

In Yucatan, in Yucatan,
Land of eternal lotus chewing,
In Yucatan, in Yucatan,
Where sunny skies are blue as bluing,
In Yucatan, in Yucatan,
Oh, land of honeyed "Nothing Doing,"
Land of lyric, love, and leisure,
Place of poetry and pleasure,
Fairy-land of "Nothing Doing"—
Yucatan—in Yucatan.

Banish we the thoughts of sorrow
In this country of the blest;
Brood we not on a to-morrow,
Life is only brief at best.
In this land of summer season,
Reck we not of rhyme or reason,
As we puff the mild cigarro,
Singing "Life's a merry jest."

In Yucatan, in Yucatan,
Land of eternal lotus chewing,
In Yucatan, in Yucatan,
Where sunny skies are blue as bluing,
In Yucatan, in Yucatan,
Oh, land of honeyed "Nothing Doing,"
Land of lyric, love, and leisure,
Place of poetry and pleasure,
Fairy-land of "Nothing Doing"—
Yucatan—in Yucatan.

The following group of five songs was probably written soon after the collaborators had received a managerial lecture on the practical requirements of the theatre. They breathe the spirit of stagy sophistication as to "what they want," and "how to get it over."

LET US SING

There is nothing new, my lady, in the lexicon of love;
It is all as old as time.
They were vowing by the moon and to the twinkling stars above,
When they handed Eve the lime.
There is nothing new to tell you, there is nothing to sing,
There is nothing new to say;
So you'll have to be contented with the ordinary thing,
In the ordinary way.

    Let us sing in the manner traditional,
    For we must have a lovers' duet,
    With a silly refrain repetitional
    In a chorus you cannot forget.
    They'll applaud from Topeka to Gloversville,

MISADVENTURES IN MUSICAL COMEDY

At the mention of "Love" or a "Kiss";
Oh, you bet we are lovers from Loversville
And we love in a lyric like this:—

LOVE IS ALL THAT MATTERS

An audience is generally clamorous,
For something in the nature of a waltz;
Be it ne'er so senseless,
Wherefore-less and whence-less,
Be its logic ne'er so full of faults,
Just let the theme and melody be amorous,
And let the honeyed sentiment be plain;
If the music's tuneful,
If the words are spoon-ful,
Love is all you need in a refrain.

For love is all that matters
In a waltz refrain—
A lilt that softly patters
Like a summer rain;
A theme that's worn to tatters;
And an ancient strain.
Yet love is all that matters
In a waltz refrain.

Now I might sing a song of high society,
And I might sing about a lot of things.
I might spend the time on
Warbling you a rhyme on
Anything from cabbages to kings.
But though I have an infinite variety
Of themes that I might sing about to you,
There is only one thing,
Though an overdone thing,
Love, the olden theme that's always new.

For love is all that matters
In a waltz refrain—
A lilt that softly patters
Like a summer rain;
A theme that's worn to tatters;
And an ancient strain.
Yet love is all that matters
In a waltz refrain.

Let who will construct a nation's laws if I may write its songs,
As the poet used to say;
Though it's absolutely simple if you figure what belongs
To the usual National lay.
Take the songs of Andalusia as presented on the stage
By a dashing young brunette,
Who can stamp her feet in anger and can snap her eyes in rage,
And can smoke a cigarette.

Let us sing in a manner Castilian
To the twang of the gladsome guitar,
With a colour scheme black and vermilion,
And the music staccato bizarre;
Let us sing all tha* sad señorita stuff
To a dance that is mildly insane;
Let us steal all that old Carmencita stuff,
That's the way of the lovers in Spain:—

CARAMBA

Spanish Burlesque Song

Caramba di Sar-sa-pa-ril-li-o,
Cinchona, Peruna, Mon-doo;
Bologna, Cologna, Vanillio,
Northwestern and eke "C. B. Q."

MISADVENTURES IN MUSICAL COMEDY

Oh, Chilli con carne and Piccolo—
Mazeppa di Buffalo Bill—
So hurry and drop in your nickel-o,
Caramba di Sar-sa-pa-rill!

Backward, turn a little backward, Father Tempus in thy flight,
To the days of long ago;
When Variety was funny and a "team" was a delight
In a biff-bang slap-stick show.
If you'll give us your attention for a moment we will try
Quite a job of comedy,
For a couple of comedians you see in she and I,
As you can quite plainly see.

Let us sing in a way vaudevillian,
In the way of the "ten-twenty-thirt"
When the "Varnishes" (Eddie and Lillian)
Make you laugh till you honestly hurt.
Let us hand out a sad little "mother" song,
In a way that is truly refined;
Let us follow it up with another song,
Of the best song-and-danciest kind:—

NEVER FORGET YOUR PARENTS

A young man once was sitting
Within a swell café,
The music it did play so sweet,
The people were so gay.
But he alone was silent,
A tear was in his eye,
A waitress she stepped up to him,
And asked him gently why.
He turned to her in sorrow,
And at first he spoke no word;
But soon he spoke unto her,

WAIFS AND STRAYS

For she was an honest girl.
He rose up from that table,
In that elegant café,
And in a voice replete with tears,
To her, he then did say:

"Never forget your father
Think all he done for you
Do not desert your mother dear,
So loving, kind, and true.
Think of all they have gave you—
Do not cast it away—
For if it had not been for them
We would not be here to-day."

WHILE STROLLING THRO' THE FOREST

While strolling thro' the forest
Upon a summer's day,
I chanced to see, and she smiled at me,
A lady and her name was May.
Oh my! Wasn't she a beaut!
Root-ti-toot, ti-toot-ti-toot-ti-toot!
She's the neatest, she's the sweetest,
She's also the completest.
She's the lady who I dearly love,
And—ah—this is—ah—what she said:

We have tried for to amuse you
With our remarks so bright,
And now that we have finished,
We're going to say good-night.
We are chatty, we are happy,
And we think the same of you,
And with your kind permission
We're going to say "Adoo."

216

MISADVENTURES IN MUSICAL COMEDY

Dear Yankee Maid, one guesses, was intended to suit the requirements of the manager's protégé, the nice-looking fellow who danced well and sang excellently; and You May Always Be My Sweetheart was a duet to be sung probably by this paragon and the leading lady.

DEAR YANKEE MAID

There's a lilt that is tuneful and fetchin'!
When you sing of an Irish colleen;
And the lyrical praise of a Gretchen
Is a theme that is fit for a queen;
The bewitching young lady of Paris—
She may hold many fast in her thrall—
But this song (which is published by Harris)
Is to tell of the best of them all.

O Yankee maid! My Yankee maid!
You are the one best bet.
You are the goods, with duty prepaid.
You are the finest yet.
I am for you, brown eyes or blue,
Tresses of gold or jet.
I serenade you, Yankee maid;
You are the one best bet.

Of the maiden seductive and Spanish,
There is many a song has been sung.
And the ladies Norwegian and Danish
Were a theme when Columbus was young;
Oh, the ladies of England are pretty;
There are those who declare for the Jap.
But the best is the girl of this ditty,
Yankee maids are the best on the map.

217

'O Yankee maid! My Yankee maid!
You are the one best bet.
You are the goods, with duty prepaid.
You are the finest yet.
I am for you, brown eyes or blue,
Tresses of gold or jet.
I serenade you, Yankee maid;
You are the one best bet.

YOU MAY ALWAYS BE MY SWEETHEART
(If You Care to Be)

A maid of simple station, I, unlearned in lovers' lore,
  Sweetly shy;
The art of osculation I had never tried before,
  Which is why
Your recent demonstration of that proud and manly art—
  Is it plain?—
Has caused a queer sensation in the region of my heart,
  And this refrain:

I've never had a sweetheart, for I've been fancy free.
My heart's been locked to lovers, and there's no key.
But if you should continue to be so kind to me,
  You may always be my sweetheart if you care to be.

Dear Madam: Contents noted in your favour of this date;
  I remain
As ever, Yours Devotedly—P. S., I beg to state
  And explain
Your recent proposition has a sweet and pleasant sound
  To my ears,
'Twill be my fond ambition just to have you stick around
  A million years.

MISADVENTURES IN MUSICAL COMEDY

I've never had a sweetheart, for I've been fancy free.
My heart's been locked to lovers, and there's no key.
But if you should continue to be so kind to me,
I will always be your sweetheart if you'll let me be.

The Statue Song was written as a substitute for one the composer was guilty of, to fit a tune which was described as "a lutherburbank of 'Anitra's Dance' in the Peer Gynt suite and Moskowski's 'Spanish Dance.'"

STATUE SONG

Idol of my race, I sing,
Humbly kneeling at thy shrine.
Take the sacrifice I bring;
All that I possess is thine:

Humbly kneeling at thy shrine,
Let me chant my idol song.
All that I possess is thine,
I have loved thee overlong,

Let me chant my idol song.
Take the sacrifice I bring.
I have loved thee overlong.
Idol of my race I sing.

Beloved let me lay these at thy feet—
These flowers of forgetfulness so sweet.
Forsake thou thoughts of other days and pride,
And come thou back with me, thine Indian bride,
Untamed and free.
Return to me
Thine own predestined bride.

Little Old Main Street is a protest and natural reaction from the wave of Broadway and Little-Old-New York songs which for so long inundated long-suffering Oshkosh and Kalamazoo.

LITTLE OLD MAIN STREET

Singers may boast about Broadway,'
And they most gen'rally do:
Spring all that flowery fluff on the Bowery—
Take it, I'll stake it to you;
Call me a yap if you care to,
Say I'm a rube or a shine,
But give me the street that has got 'em all beat—
Little old Main Street for mine.

Little old Main Street for mine!
Take a look at the lovers in line—
Three village charmers and twenty-eight farmers,
All meeting the six-twenty-nine—
Little old Main Street for mine,
When you're back with the pigs and the kine,
Broadway and such for Your Uncle?   Not much
For it's Little old Main Street for mine.

Sing if you must of your State Street,
Sing of the Bois and the Strand,
And if you have a new song of the Avenue,
Sing it to beat the old band!
Sing of the streets of the city,
Not for Yours Truly—"Uh, Uh!"
But give me the street of the village élite;
Little old Main Street for *muh* !

Little old Main Street for mine,
And right down by the Post Office sign
Hear 'em say "Well, what a long rainy spell!
But it looks like to-morrow'll be fine."
Little old Main Street for mine,
Where it's dead at a quarter past nine
See the folks flock past the Opry-House block,
Oh, it's little old Main Street for mine.

"It's the Little Things that Count," even in the success of a musical comedy. A few trifles like the following would have gone far toward making a Broadway success.

IT'S THE LITTLE THINGS THAT COUNT

Girl —Little drops of water, little grains of sand,
     Make the mighty ocean and the pleasant land
Boy— Little drops of seltzer, little drops of rye,
     Make the pleasant highball, when a man is dry.
Both—It's the little things that count, ev'rywhere you go;
     Trifles make a large amount, Don't you find it so?
Girl —Little deeds of kindness, little words of love,
     Make our life an Eden, like the heaven above.
Boy— Little drops of promise, made to little wives,
     Make us little fibbers all our little lives.
Both—It's the little things that count, ev'rywhere you go;
     Trifles make a large amount.   Don't you find it so?

the human machine—all of which subsequently found their way into his stories. Some of his adventures while Haroun-al-Raschiding must, therefore, possess interest for the vast reading throng that has smiled and felt a tear while turning his pages. It was during one of his prowling tours several years ago that O. Henry, with H. H. McClure, who suggested the writing of the modern Arabian Nights tales to the short-story king, was seated in a Broadway restaurant at luncheon. "What are you going to do tonight?" asked McClure. "I'm going to persuade a 'hobo' to give me three hundred dollars," answered the writer. "On a bet?" asked McClure. "Not at all," replied O. Henry, "that's the price of a story and I'm going to rub up against some tramps down on the Bowery until one of them suggests the plot to me." That night O. Henry did travel downtown and started on a Haroun-al-Raschid expedition in the vicinity of the famous bread-line. His genial, well-fleshed personality always stood him in good stead, and no matter how tough the community he chanced to enter, unpleasantness of any sort was a rare occurrence. When he talked with a "hobo" he was a "hobo." When he talked with a railroad president he was a railroad president. O. Henry was a chameleon of conversation and of what is known colloquially as "front." He always took on the air—it seemed—of the person to whom he was talking. One of his friends has said of him that there was no better "mixer" in the world—and the truth of the

statement is borne out by a survey of the intimate
and varied insight revealed in his diverse writings.
On the night in question O. Henry moved around
among the Bowery derelicts until he finally got into
touch with a typical "bum." They strolled down
the street a way together and asked a passer-by
for the time. "Almost midnight," said the latter.
"Gee," remarked Henry to his tattered companion.
"I feel like a cup o' coffee. Come on, I've got a
quarter and we'll blow some of it in this place."
They entered the dingy eating-house, sat up to the
counter and each ordered a cup of coffee and a ham
sandwich. Although the two men had now been
together for some time, the short-story writer had
detected the gleam of nothing definite in the tramp
that promised to provide the "copy" he was seeking.
But he felt sure he had picked his man right and he
felt equally sure that the fellow sooner or later would
unconsciously suggest to him something or other by
which he would profit. O. Henry rarely "led" the
conversation. He preferred to let it come naturally.
He said nothing to his companion, who was busily
concerning himself with the food before him. When
they had finished and had reached the street, Henry
suggested that they walk leisurely up the Bowery
and see if there was anything to be seen. They
wandered around aimlessly for fully an hour and a half
and then Henry said he felt like having another cup
of coffee. The two men went into another eating-
place and ordered two cups of coffee—at two cents a

cup. Then they walked around some more, but still Henry had succeeded in getting no idea from his bedraggled companion. Finally, tired out, he told the latter he was going to leave him. He reached out his hand to "shake" with the tramp and, as their hands met, Henry suddenly surprised the "hobo" by laughing. "What's up, cull?" asked the latter. "Oh, nothin'," replied Henry, "I just thought of something." This was true, as he afterward confessed, the "something" in point having been an odd twist for a new story. But the oddest twist to this particular Haroun-al-Raschid anecdote —and a typical O. Henry twist it is—is the fact that the idea O. Henry suddenly got for his story had absolutely nothing to do with the Bowery, with tramps, with two-cent coffee, or anything even remotely related thereto. "Well, then," remarked a friend to whom he had narrated the incident, "what good did the Bowery sojourn do you? You didn't get your three-hundred-dollar idea from a tramp after all, did you?"

"Indeed, I did," replied O. Henry. "That is, in a way. The tramp didn't give me the idea, to be sure, but he did not drive it out of my head—which is just as important. If I had not gone down on the Bowery and had chosen an uptown friend for a companion instead of that tramp, my more cultured companion would not have allowed me a moment's conversational respite in which my mind could have worked, and, as a consequence, the idea would never have come to me. So, you see, the Bowery 'hobo' served a lot of good, after all."

Strolling through Madison Square one night after the theatre, O. Henry came upon a young girl crying as if her heart were surely cracking, if not already broken. The man with Henry, his pity and sympathy aroused, walked over to the girl, touched her on the shoulder, and inquired into the cause of her grief. It developed that the girl had come to the city from a town in central New Jersey, had lost her way, and was without money, friends, or a place to sleep. Deeply touched, the man with the short-story writer gave the girl a couple of dollars, put her in charge of a policeman, whose latent sympathy he managed to arouse with a one-dollar bill, and, satisfied with his act of charity, locked arms with Henry and continued on through the dark square toward Twenty-third Street. "Why didn't you speak to her?" he asked Henry. "I'll bet there was a corking story in that girl that you could have dragged out." O. Henry smiled. "Old man," he said, "there never is a story where there seems to be one. That's one rule I always work on—it saves time and, let me see—two plus one—yes, three dollars!"

O. Henry's metropolitan sales- and shop-girl types are well known to his readers. "Do you ever go into the department stores to study them?" some one once asked the writer. "Indeed, not," answered the latter. "It is not the sales-girl in the department store who is worth studying, it is the sales-girl out of it.   You can't get romance over a counter."

With two friends O. Henry was walking down Broadway one evening in December—Broadway, the sack of New York "life," the big paper Bagdad out of which O. Henry drew many of his characters. Near Herald Square the men were approached by a rather well-dressed young man who, in a calm, gentle voice, told his "hard luck story" and begged for the "loan" of a quarter.   One of the men handed over the twenty-five cents to the stranger and the latter disappeared quickly 'round the corner into Thirty-sixth Street.   "Seemed like an honest, worthy chap," remarked the man who had parted with the quarter.   "Yes," added O. Henry quietly, "he seemed like an honest, worthy chap to me, too—last night."

While walking down Broadway on another occasion, O. Henry accidentally bumped against a man who was not looking in the direction he was walking. "I beg your pardon," said Henry, "but really you ought to look where you are going."   "If I did in this town, I probably wouldn't go," replied the man with a sarcastic smile.   "Ah," said O. Henry quickly, "and how are all the folks in Chicago?"

When O. Henry collaborated with F. P. Adams in writing the libretto for the musical comedy "Lo," a friend said to him: "Adams says he got the idea for his share of the play from a cheque for advance royalties.   Where did you get the idea for your share?"

"From the *hope* for a cheque for advance royalties," he answered.

While "Harouning" along the river front one night, O. Henry happened upon a couple of sailors, one of whom was much the worse for liquor. "I see your friend is intoxicated," he remarked to the sober sailor. "You don't say!" exclaimed the latter in mock astonishment. And the short-story king appreciated the answer at his expense as much as did those to whom he subsequently repeated it. O. Henry never missed a favourable opportunity to have a chat with an amiable policeman. "Policemen know so many odd things and so few necessary ones," he would remark. While talking with one of the blue-coats in Hell's Kitchen one night, years ago, Henry said that they were suddenly startled—at least, that he was—by two loud revolver shots. "Some one's been killed!" he exclaimed. "No, don't worry," returned the "cop" coolly, "only injured. It takes at least three bullets to kill any one in this part of town."

O. HENRY—APOTHECARY*

By Christopher Morley

WHERE once he used camphor, glycerin,
  Cloves, aloes, potash, peppermint in bars,
  And all the oils and essences so keen
That druggists keep in rows of stoppered jars—
Now, blender of strange drugs more volatile,
  The master pharmacist of joy and pain
Dispenses sadness tinctured with a smile
  And laughter that dissolves in tears again.

O brave apothecary! You who knew
  What dark and acid doses life prefers,
And yet with smiling face resolved to brew
  These sparkling potions for your customers—
Glowing with globes of red and purple glass
  Your window gladdens travellers who pass.

---

* From a volume of Mr. Morley's poems published by the George H. Doran Company.

O. HENRY*

By William Lyon Phelps

IN North Carolina they have just erected a memorial to "O.Henry." He was a profoundly sincere artist, as is shown, not only in his finished work but in his private correspondence. His worst defect was a fear and hatred of conventionality; he had such mortal terror of stock phrases that, as some one has said, he wrote no English at all—he wrote the dot, dash, telegraphic style. Yet leaving aside all his perversities and his whimsicalities, and the poorer part of his work where the desire to be original is more manifest than any valuable result of it, there remain a sufficient number of transcripts from life and interpretations of it to give him abiding fame. There is a humorous tenderness in The Whirligig of Life,† and profound ethical passion in A Blackjack Bargainer.† A highly intelligent though unfavourable criticism of Porter that came to me in a private letter —I wish it might be printed—condemns him for the vagaries of his plots—which remind my correspondent of the quite serious criticism he read in a Philadelphia newspaper, which spoke of "the interesting but hardly credible adventures of Ulysses." Now

---

* From "The Advance of the English Novel," by William Lyon Phelps, Dodd, Mead & Co., 1916.
† See "Whirligigs."

hyperbole is a great American failing; and Porter was so out and out American that this disease of art raised blotches on his work. Yet his best emphasis is placed where it belongs.

No writer of distinction has, I think, been more closely identified with the short story in English than O. Henry. Irving, Poe, Hawthorne, Bret Harte, Stevenson, Kipling attained fame in other fields; but although Porter had his mind fully made up to launch what he hoped would be the great American novel, the veto of death intervened, and the many volumes of his "complete works" are made up of brevities. The essential truthfulness of his art is what gave his work immediate recognition, and accounts for his rise from journalism to literature. There is poignancy in his pathos; desolation in his tragedy; and his extraordinary humour is full of those sudden surprises that give us delight. Uncritical readers have never been so deeply impressed with O. Henry as have the professional, jaded critics, weary of the old trick a thousand times repeated, who found in his writings a freshness and originality amounting to genius.

ABOUT NEW YORK WITH O. HENRY

By Arthur Bartlett Maurice

I

THE HEART OF O'HENRY-LAND

IRVING PLACE, beginning at Fourteenth Street, runs north for six blocks to perish against the iron palings that line the southerly side of Gramercy Park. Half way up, on the west side of the thoroughfare, between Seventeenth and Eighteenth streets, there is a dingy, four-story, brownstone house. The shutters are up. The casements of the upper stories frame vacancy. That vacancy stares down at the passer-by with a kind of hurt blindness. It is as if the structure itself was conscious of an imminent demise, of a swiftly coming demolition. For next year, next month, next week, to-morrow, perhaps, the old ramshackle edifice will be gone, with a towering skyscraper springing up on the site. The number of the building is 55. There, in the front room on the second floor, William Sydney Porter lived in the days when he was learning to read the heart of the Big City of Razzle-Dazzle. And as he was constitutionally opposed to anything that involved arduous physical exercise, the quintessence of O'Henry-

233

Land lies within a circle of half a mile radius, with No. 55 as the centre.

Within that circle may be found the hotels of the Spanish-American New York stories, Chubbs' Third Avenue Restaurant, the Old Munich of The Halberdier of the Little Rheinschloss,* the particular saloon which served as the background for The Lost Blend†—as a matter of fact that saloon is directly across the street from No. 55 and behind the bar there presides a white-aproned, genial cocktail mixer who will answer to the name of "Con" just as in the story—the four sides of Gramercy Park which are so conspicuous in the tales of aristocratic flavour, the bench—which could be confused with no other bench in the world—which Stuffy Pete, one of Two Thanksgiving-day Gentlemen,‡ regarded in the light of personal property, and those other benches in the other square, a few blocks to the north, where prepossessing young women, inspired by Robert Louis Stevenson's "New Arabian Nights," were moved to romantic narrative, where disconsolate caliphs, shorn of their power, sat brooding over the judgments of Allah, where fifth wheels rolled along asphalted pavements and djinns came obedient to the rubbing of the lamp.

To Mr. Robert Rudd Whiting, with whom he had been associated in the early days when he first began

* See "Roads of Destiny."
† See "The Trimmed Lamp."
‡ See "The Trimmed Lamp."

to contribute to the columns of *Ainslee's Magazine*, Sydney Porter once extended a luncheon invitation. It was to be a Spanish-American luncheon in the course of which O. Henry was to introduce his guest to certain flavours and dishes that he, himself, had learned to like or at least to endure in the days of his exile in the Lands of the Lotus Eaters. The two men were crossing Union Square. "Come with me," said Porter, "I will show you the real place. Over at M——'s [he mentioned a restaurant in a street to the south] you may find the Señors, the Capitans, the Majors, the Colonels. But if you would sit with the Generalissimos, the Imperators, the truly exalted who hail from Central and South American countries, accept my guiding hand." So from the Square they turned in Fifteenth Street and found, on the south side, some seventy-five yards east of Fourth Avenue, the Hotel America, with its clientele of gesticulating Latins, who, if not planning revolution, had all the outward appearance of arch-conspirators. It was the atmosphere that went to the making of The Gold that Glittered,* which, if the reader remembers, began at the very spot at which the invitation had been extended "where Broadway skirts the corner of the Square presided over by George the Veracious."

The Halberdier of the Little Rheinschloss† dealt with a restaurant which O. Henry designated

---

* See "Strictly Business."
† See "Roads of Destiny."

as Old Munich.   Long ago, the story-teller told us,
it was the resort of interesting Bohemians, but now
"only artists and musicians and literary folk fre-
quent it."   For many years, so the tale runs, the
customers of Old Munich have accepted the place
as a faithful copy from the ancient German town.
The big hall, with its smoky rafters, rows of im-
ported steins, portrait of Goethe, and verses printed
on the walls—translated into German from the original of the Cincinnati Poets—seemed atmospheric-
ally correct when viewed through the bottom of a
glass.   Then the proprietors rented the room above,
called it the Little Rheinschloss, and built in a stair-
way.   Up there was an imitation stone parapet,
ivy-covered, and the walls painted to represent depth
and distance, with the Rhine winding at the base of
the vineyarded slopes and the Castle of Ehrenbreit-
stein looming directly opposite the entrance.   To
Old Munich came the young man with the wrecked
good clothes and the hungry look, to assume the
armour of the ancient halberdier and, on a certain
momentous evening, to be confiscated by the aristocrats to serve menially at the banquet-board.

As the tale had always been an especial favourite,
the present writer had ventured into many parts of
the city in his search for the background that would
best fit the O. Henry description.   For a time the
hunt seemed vain.   But one day he spoke to Mr.
Gilman Hall on the subject.   The latter laughed.
"Do I know the real Old Munich?   Very well, in-

deed. Often I dined there with Porter. No wonder
you have not found it. You have been looking too
far to the north, to the south, to the west. Don't
you realize that Porter would never have walked that
far if he could have helped it? The only time I ever
persuaded him afoot as far as Seventy-second Street
and Riverside Drive, he stopped, and, with an injured
air, asked if we had not yet passed Peekskill. We
are just before his old home, No. 55. Why not try
round the corner?" So fifty feet to the south, and a
short block to the east, in the restaurant and beer-
hall known to some as Allaire's and to others as
Scheffel Hall, the setting of the tale was found. There
was a natural free-hand swing to certain parts of the
O. Henry descriptions, but even without the cor-
roboration of those who knew personally of Porter's
associations with the place, one glance at the long
raftered room is enough to stamp it as the place where
the waiter known simply as No. 18 witnessed the
comedy of the hot soup tureen and the blistered
hands, and William Deering finished the three
months of earning his own living without once being
discharged for incompetence

II

THE O. HENRY APPEAL

Three or four years ago, in the columns of a literary magazine of which he was then the editor, the
present writer invited the expression of various opin-

237

ions with the idea of finding out which of the stories
of O. Henry had had the widest appeal.   To the person whom he then designated as The Thousandth
Reader he presented ten volumes of the short stories.
She was being introduced for the first time to the
work of O. Henry, and for a month, day after day,
she gave herself over to the two hundred and fifty
odd tales of the modern Scheherazade.   When she
had finished the last story he asked her to jot down
the names of the ten that had most appealed to her,
in the order of their appeal.   Her choice was in many
ways so surprising that it suggested the symposium.
This was the list of The Thousandth Reader:

1. A Municipal Report.
2. The Pendulum.
3. A Blackjack Bargainer.
4. A Retrieved Reformation.
5. The Furnished Room.
6. The Hypotheses of Failure.
7. Roads of Destiny.
8. Next to Reading Matter.
9. The Enchanted Profile.
10. Two Renegades.

To that list the present writer decided to add nine
others.   First were three from men who were themselves spinners of tales.   Booth Tarkington, Owen
Johnson, and George Barr McCutcheon.

Mr. Tarkington, commenting upon his list, said:
"The ten are not his best stories.   I don't know
which his 'best' are, of course.   These ten are what

you asked for—the ten I have enjoyed most. There is one I wanted to include. The boy who went to war after the girl flouted him and came back the town hero and said to her (she was married then): 'Oh, I don't know—maybe I could if I tried!' but I couldn't remember the title and couldn't find it." (The title of the story Mr. Tarkington had in mind was The Moment of Victory in "Options.")

Mr. Tarkington's list:

1. The Ransom of Red Chief.
2. The Harbinger.
3. The Passing of Black Eagle.
4. Squaring the Circle.
5. Past One at Rooney's.
6. The Handbook of Hymen.
7. Strictly Business.
8. The Clarion Call.
9. Jeff Peters as a Personal Magnet.
10. The Memento.

The following titles represented the choice of Mr. Owen Johnson:

1. An Unfinished Story.
2. A Municipal Report.
3. The Rose of Dixie.
4. A Lickpenny Lover.
5. According to Their Lights.
6. Mammon and the Archer.
7. The Defeat of the City.
8. The Girl and the Graft.
9. The Shamrock and the Palm.
10. The Pendulum.

Mr. George Barr McCutcheon's list:

1. The Tale of a Tainted Tenner.
2. Let Me Feel Your Pulse.
3. A Fog in Santone.
4. The Lost Blend.
5. The Duplicity of Hargraves.
6. The Marquis and Miss Sally.
7. The Gift of the Magi.
8. A Cosmopolite in a Café.
9. According to Their Lights.
10. The Making of a New Yorker.

Fifth in order, but naturally first in sentimental interest, was the list indicating the feelings of The One Who Knew Him Best—Mrs. William Sydney Porter. It was in a very beautiful letter that Mrs. Porter told of her preferences. To her the stories *were* Mr. Porter. She found it hard to name them in a list in order. But immediately one story came to her mind. That was A Municipal Report.*

"After all," she wrote, "I am not sure that it is the story—good as it is—for O. Henry's own face lifts from a Nashville 'roast' that was given that story and I hear his puzzled, 'Why did it offend? Do you see anything in it that should offend?' The Fifth Wheel†—and we stand together on Madison Square in the deep snow, or the biting wind, looking at the line waiting for beds. When we turn away ten men have found shelter. The recording angel

---

* See "Strictly Business."
† See "Strictly Business."

must have seen us there some of the snowy nights of 1908. He must have known that when we turned homeward there were times when O. Henry had not a dollar fifty left in his pocket." One story in Mrs. Porter's list likely to surprise readers is Madame Bo-Peep of the Ranches.* But Mrs. Porter said that that story figured largely in her own life. In the spring of 1905 her mother came home from Greensboro and said to her: "Your old friend Will Porter is a writer. He lives in New York and writes under the name of O. Henry." "O. Henry! In my desk lay Madame Bo-Peep and I loved her. I wrote O. Henry a note. 'If you are not Will Porter don't bother to answer,' I said. He bothered to answer. The letter came as fast as Uncle Sam could bring it. 'Some day when you are not real busy,' he wrote, 'won't you sit down at your desk where you keep those antiquated stories and write to me? I'd be so pleased to hear something about what the years have done for you, and what you think about when the tree frogs begin to holler in the evening.' Thus after many years a boy and girl friendship was renewed. Last in my list, but first in my heart, is Adventures in Neurasthenia, the new title, Let Me Feel Your Pulse,† the publishers gave. It brings back the little office in Asheville, the pad, empty except for the title and the words: 'So I went to a doctor.' So often at the last the pad was empty.

---

* See "Whirligigs."
† See "Sixes and Sevens."

The sharp pencil points in their waiting seemed to me to mock the empty pencil, the weary brain. The picture is too vivid." This was Mrs. Porter's list:

1. A Municipal Report.
2. The Fifth Wheel.
3. A Lickpenny Lover.
4. A Doubledyed Deceiver.
5. Brickdust Row.
6. The Trimmed Lamp.
7. The Brief Début of 'Tildy.
8. An Unfinished Story.
9. Madame Bo-Peep of the Ranches.
10. Let Me Feel Your Pulse.

The sixth list was from a man (incidentally he was one of O. Henry's closest friends in the New York years) who has read, accepted, and rejected more short stories than any other man in the world. That man was Mr. Robert H. Davis, and among the accepted stories were many of the stories of O. Henry. Prefacing his selection, Mr. Davis expressed the opinion that The Last Leaf* would become more impressive as he grew older, whereas at the time of writing A Tempered Wind † and An Unfinished Story ‡ entertained him greatly. There were times when he laughed inordinately at The Handbook of Hymen § and Hostages to Momus.** "It is rather

* See "The Trimmed Lamp."
† See "The Gentle Grafter."
‡ See "The Four Million."
§ See "Heart of the West."
** See "The Gentle Grafter."

remarkable," wrote Mr. Davis, "that a man of his temperament could do so many good stories under the high pressure of necessity. He was buoyant and lazy in prosperity, depressed and productive in adversity. How few of the millions who read him know what it cost O. Henry to make them laugh!" These were the ten tales that had been caught in the meshes of Mr. Davis's memory:

1. A Tempered Wind.
2. The Last Leaf.
3. An Unfinished Story.
4. Hostages to Momus.
5. The Trimmed Lamp.
6. Friend Telemachus.
7. The Handbook of Hymen.
8. The Moment of Victory.
9. The Ethics of Pig.
10. A Technical Error.

The following list made by Mr. Arthur W. Page represents, in a measure, the opinion of Mr. Porter's publishers:

1. The Rose of Dixie.
2. The Gift of the Magi.
3. The Cop and the Anthem.
4. Let Me Feel Your Pulse.
5. An Unfinished Story.
6. A Municipal Report.
7. The Guardian of the Accolade.
8. Witches' Loaves.
9. Hearts and Crosses.
10. The Fifth Wheel.

WAIFS AND STRAYS

Many persons have come forward claiming to have discovered O. Henry. Some of these claims have come from sources that would have moved Sydney Porter himself to mingled delight and astonishment. But the man who was responsible for O. Henry's going to New York, who persuaded the publisher of a magazine to forward the money that made the journey possible, was Mr. Gilman Hall. So among all claimants Mr. Hall has the best title to recognition as O. Henry's discoverer. Mr. Hall's list:

1. An Unfinished Story.
2. A Municipal Report.
3. Roads of Destiny.
4. The Buyer from Cactus City.
5. The Furnished Room.
6. The Passing of Black Eagle.
7. The Gift of the Magi.
8. From the Cabby's Seat.
9. Brickdust Row.
10. A Retrieved Reformation.

To the opinions of writers of stories and buyers of stories it was thought wise to add the point of view of those whose business it is to sell stories. Three literary agents were consulted. This is a composite list representing their opinions:

1. A Harlem Tragedy.
2. Mammon and the Archer
3. A Lickpenny Lover.
4. The Furnished Room.
5. The Marry Month of May.

6. The Gift of the Magi.
7. The Enchanted Profile.
8. An Unfinished Story.
9. The Last Leaf.
10. The Thing's the Play.

In conclusion the present writer insisted in presenting a list indicating his own favourites. It was as follows:

1. The Defeat of the City.
2. Mammon and the Archer.
3. The Furnished Room.
4. The Shamrock and the Palm.
5. The Halberdier of the Rheinschloss.
6. The Lost Blend.
7. A Lickpenny Lover.
8. A Municipal Report.
9. Two Renegades.
10. Thimble, Thimble.

Curious indeed, is the story told by these lists. It illustrates strikingly the wide range of O. Henry's appeal. Ten lists of ten tales apiece, and sixty-two different titles, most of them appearing on but one list. A few favourites there are: A Municipal Report* (the narrative which probably shows its author at the highwater mark of his powers) with six mentions; An Unfinished Story† with seven mentions; A Lickpenny Lover,‡ The Gift of the Magi,† and The Furnished Room,† with four mentions; and The Mammon and the Archer† and

* See "Strictly Business."
† See "The Four Million."
‡ See "The Voice of the City."

Let Me Feel Your Pulse* with three mentions. On the basis of these lists the New York stories have had the greatest appeal. Some of the individual selections were significant. For example, Mr. Tarkington picked as his first choice The Ransom of Red Chief,† a tale to be found in no other list. Perhaps that was only the expression of the mood of a moment, the liking of a man who during the previous two or three years had invented Hedrick Madison and Penrod Schofield for a delightfully diabolical boy.

III

THE "EAST SIDE" OF O. HENRY

In his nightly wanderings through his City of Bagdad, the good Haroun-al-Raschid in his golden prime did not confine himself to those thoroughfares that were analogous to London's Park Lane, Paris's Avenue Bois de Boulogne, or New York's Riverside Drive. On the contrary, he preferred to seek out the purlieus, and to listen wisely in the humble shop of "Fitbad the Tailor." Likewise the Haroun-al-Raschid of the modern Bagdad-on-the-Subway. The Editor-man, or more likely two or three of him, would be waiting for the promised (and in many cases already paid for) story, so Sydney Porter would say good-bye to the companions with whom he was sitting in a Broadway restaurant, proceed downtown, and stroll along the

* See "Sixes and Sevens."

† See "Whirligigs."

Bowery or adjacent streets until he fell in with the
particular tramp who seemed most promising as copy.
Sometimes he found the story and sometimes he did
not. Often, when the idea came, it had absolutely
nothing to do with the Bowery, or with tramps, or
with two-cent coffee, or with anything remotely
related thereto. But to Sydney Porter that was no
reason for withholding the credit he considered due
to the tramp. "He did not give me the idea," he
once said in explanation, "but he did not drive it out
of my head—which is just as important."

Whether the particular tramp of an evening's
ramble meant the inked pages of a tale of Texas, or
Central America, or New Orleans, O. Henry's wanderings about the East Side are reflected in some
twenty or thirty stories with very definite back-
grounds. The care with which Porter sought his
local colour is indicated in The Sleuths,* in which
a man from the Middle West goes to New York to
find his sister. At her address he learns that she
has moved away a month before, leaving no clue, and
to help in the search he enlists the services of the
famous detectives Mullins & Shamrock Jolnes.
The science of deduction leads to No. 12 Avenue C,
which is described as an "old-fashioned brownstone
house in a prosperous and respectable neighbourhood." Now, if any neighbourhood in New York
City is not prosperous and respectable, it is that
about Avenue C and Second Street. The Mulberry

---

* See "Sixes and Sevens."

Bend of other years was hardly more unsightly and unkempt. O. Henry had sensed its offensiveness through his eyes and his nostrils. The selection of the No. 12 was not mere chance. He knew that there was no such number: that on the southeast corner was a saloon bearing the number 10, and on the northeast corner the pharmacy was designated as No. 14. Just as there is no No. 13 Washington Square, there is no No. 12 Avenue C. Also there is no No. 162 Chilton Street, where the missing sister was eventually found, for the reason that in the Borough of Manhattan there is no Chilton Street at all.

Somewhere on the East Side is the famous Café Maginnis, where Ikey Snigglefritz, in the proudest, maddest moment of his life shook the hand of the great Billy McMahon. An indication as to the Café Maginnis's exact whereabouts is given in the information that Ikey, leaving it, "went down Hester Street, and up Chrystie and down Delancey to where he lived. Ikey's home was in a crazy brick structure, "foul and awry," and there Cortlandt Van Duykinck found him and shook his hand, thereby completing the social triangle. There somewhere was the saloon of Dutch Mike where the Mulberry Hill gang and the Dry Dock gang met in the Homeric conflict the outcome of which sent Cork McManus to strange lands west of the Bowery and the adventures narrated in Past One at Rooney's.* There may be found the Second Avenue boarding-house

---

*See "Strictly Business."

where Miss Conway showed Andy Donovan the locket containing the portrait of her purely imaginary lover (The Count and the Wedding Guest) *. Between the Bowery and First Avenue, where the distance between the two streets is the shortest, was the Blue Light Drug Store, where Ikey Schoenstein† concocted the love philtre that was to work the downfall of his rival, Chunk Macgowan. In Orchard Street were the rooms of the Give and Take Athletic Association where, as told in The Coming Out of Maggie, ‡ Tony Spinelli played Prince Charming at the ball of the Clover Leaf Social Club under the pseudonym of Terry O'Sullivan; and farther up on the East Side, over against the elevated portion of the railroad, were the Beersheba Flats, from which the variegated tenants were driven forth by official edict to the grass of the park, and The City of Dreadful Night. ‡

IV

"HE SAW NO LONGER A RABBLE, BUT HIS BROTHERS SEEKING THE IDEAL"

To look at the matter in its chronological aspect, the first appearance of New York in the romance of O. Henry was probably in the last part of "Cabbages and Kings." There is a picture of two men sitting on a stringer of a North River pier while

* See "The Trimmed Lamp."
† See "The Four Million."
‡ See "The Voice of the City.'

a steamer from the tropics is unloading bananas and oranges. One of the men is O'Day, formerly of the Columbia Detective Agency. In a moment of confidence he tells his companion of the mistake which has brought him to his unenviable condition, and incidentally clears up for the reader the rather ugly mystery that throughout the book obscured the marriage of Frank Goodwin and the lady known in Coralio as Isabel Guilbert. To begin in another way, that is at the gateway of the city and of the new world, in the story The Lady Higher Up,* O. Henry pictures a dialogue between Mrs. Liberty, on her pedestal in the bay, and Miss Diana at the top of the tower of Madison Square Garden. Even the thick brogue which Mrs. Liberty has acquired cannot hide her envy of the other lady. In the matron's opinion Miss Diana has the best job for a statue in the whole town, with the Cat Show, and the Horse Show, and the military tournaments where the privates "look grand as generals, and the generals try to look grand as floorwalkers," and the Sportsman's Show, and above all, the French Ball "where the original Cohens and the Robert Emmet-Sangerbund Society dance the Highland Fling one with another."

But even before his first glimpse at Mrs. Liberty the visitor from a foreign shore has a sight of O. Henry's New York, as, from the deck of the transatlantic liner, the great wheels and towers of Coney

---

* See "Sixes and Sevens."

Island are pointed out to him. Among these wheels
and towers Alexander Blinker, the owner of Brick
Dust Row,* walked with Florence, his chance acquaintance of the boat, learned a lesson, and saw a
light. No more was the jostling crowd a mass of
vulgarians seeking gross joys. Counterfeit and false
though the garish pleasures of the spangled temples
were, he perceived that deep under the gilt surface
they offered saving and apposite balm and satisfaction to the restless human heart. Here, at least,
was the husk of Romance, the empty but shining
casque of Chivalry, the breath-catching though safe-
guarded dip and flight of Adventure. He saw no
longer a rabble, but his brothers seeking the ideal.
Again here, in the enchanted chicken coop of Madame
Zozo, there was reading of Tobin's Palm,† and
prophecies of a dark man and a light woman, of
trouble and financial loss, of a voyage by water, and
of a meeting with a man with a crooked nose. In
The Greater Coney‡ Dennis Carnahan expatiated
ironically on the new city which has risen, Phœnix-
like, out of the ashes of the old, and the wiping-out
process, which, to his way of thinking, consisted of
raising the price of admission from ten to twenty-
five cents, and having a blonde named Maudie to
take tickets instead of Micky, the Bowery Bite. The
Babylonian towers and the Hindoo roof gardens blaz-

---

* See "The Trimmed Lamp."
† See "The Four Million."
‡ See "Sixes and Sevens."

ing with lights, the camels moving with undulating
walk, and the tawdry gondolas of artificial Venetian
streets. These were what Mazie knew—Mazie of
A Lickpenny Lover.* These things her little soul
of a shop-girl saw when the millionaire painter-
traveller Irving Carter, whose heart she had so
strangely won, proposed to her and drew his elo-
quent picture of a honeymoon in lands beyond the
seas. These and no more. The next day her chum
in the store asks about her "swell friend." "Him,"
is the retort. "Oh, he's a cheap skate. He ain't in
it no more. What do you suppose that guy wanted
me to do? He wanted me to marry him and go to
Coney Island for a wedding trip."

A Lickpenny Lover is just one of the stories in
which the specified location is not merely a scene of
the tale, but partly an explanation of it. For example, the next time that the reader of these notes
happens to be at that point of New York City where
Sixth Avenue, Broadway, and Thirty-fourth Street
meet, let him recall Mammon and the Archer.†
In that story O. Henry is at his O. Henriest. Listen.
The last opportunity that the hero of the story, Richard Rockwell, was to have to see Miss Lantry before
her departure the next day for a two years' absence
in Europe, was to be in the hansom cab in which he
was to take her from the Grand Central Station to a
box party at Wallack's Theatre. His father, the old

---

*See "The Voice of the City."
† See "The Four Million."

soap manufacturer, cheered him with expression of rough optimism and offered to back him with his money. His aunt gave him as an amulet his mother's wedding ring in wishing him God-speed and success. Robert took the ring and started out on knightly quest. As the cab approached the crossing indicated the ring dropped tinkling to the pavement. In the few minutes' resulting delay the traffic assumed a tangled condition which held hero and heroine prisoners for hours, and late that night the boy's aunt went to the father with the news that the young people were engaged, and a warning that he should never boast of the power of money again, as the little gold band, an emblem of love and loyalty, had done what mere wealth could not accomplish. The story should have ended there, but with the characteristic touch, O. Henry introduced into the soap manufacturer's office the next morning a man who wore a red necktie and who answered to the name of Kelly. "Well," says the millionaire, "it was a pretty good bilin' of soap and how much do I owe you?" To which Kelly makes the reply that he has had five thousand dollars on account, that he had got the express wagons and cabs mostly for five dollars, but that the truckmen and motormen cost him ten dollars apiece, and the policemen twenty-five and fifty, "but," he adds enthusiastically, "when I got through I had a stage setting that would have made David Belasco envious. Why, a snake couldn't have got across Thirty-fourth Street."

WAIFS AND STRAYS

V

It is not likely that the Fourth Avenue of to-day
would have had much to appeal to O. Henry's imagination. As it was half a dozen years ago it was one
of his favourite thoroughfares, and reached its apothe-
osis in A .Bird of Bagdad.* There O. Henry pictured it as a street that the city seemed to have forgotten in its growth, a street, born and bred in the
Bowery, staggering northward full of good resolu-
tions. At Fourteenth Street "it struts for a brief
moment proudly in the glare of the museums and
cheap theatres. It may yet become a fit mate for
its highborn sister boulevard to the west, or its roaring, polyglot, broad-waisted cousin to the east."
Then it passes what O. Henry in The Gold That
Glittered,† called "the square presided over by
George the Veracious," and comes to the silent and
terrible mountains, buildings square as forts, high as
the clouds, shutting out the sky, where thousands
of slaves bend over desks all day. Next it glides
into a mediæval solitude. On each side are the shops
devoted to antiques. "Men in rusting armour stand
in the windows and menace the hurrying cars with
raised, rusty iron bumpers, hauberks, and helms,
blunderbuses, Cromwellian breastplates, matchlocks,
creeses, and the swords and daggers of an army of

* See "Strictly Business."
† See "Strictly Business."

dead and gone gallants gleam dully in the ghostly light." This mediæval solitude forbodes an early demise. What street could live inclosed by these mortuary relics and trod by these spectral citizens? "Not Fourth Avenue. Not after the tinsel but enlivening glory of the Little Rialto—not after the echoing drum beats of Union Square. There need be no tears, ladies and gentlemen. 'Tis but the suicide of a street. With a shriek and a crash Fourth Avenue dives headlong into the tunnel at Thirty-fourth Street and is never seen again."

Three of the city squares, Madison Square, Union Square, and Gramercy Park play conspicuous parts in O. Henry's stories. His tales are full of human derelicts and where is there a more natural background for such than the public benches of these parks? He shows you the Bed Liners stamping their freezing feet, and the preacher standing on a pine box exhorting his transient and shifting audience. In this Bed Line were Walter Smuythe and the discharged coachman, Thomas McQuade, the night that the red motor car, humming up Fifth Avenue, lost its extra tire as narrated in The Fifth Wheel.* It was on a bench of the Square that the millionaire Pilkins found the penniless young eloping couple, Marcus Clayton of Roanoke County, Virginia, and Eva Bedford of Bedford County, of the same State. It was perhaps on the same bench that Soapy sat meditating just what violation of the law would in-

---

* See "Strictly Business."

sure his deportation to the hospitable purlieus of Black-well's Island, which was his Palm Beach and Riviera for the winter months. It was near by at least that Prince Michael, of the Electorate of Valle Luna, known otherwise as Dopey Mike, looked up at the clock in the Metropolitan Tower and gave sage advice and consolation to the young man who was waiting to learn his fate as told in The Caliph, Cupid and the Clock.* While the auto with the white body and the red running gear was waiting near the corner of Twenty-sixth Street and Fifth Avenue, Parkenstacker made the acquaintance of the girl in gray and listened to the strange story born in the pages of Robert Louis Stevenson's "New Arabian Nights." Over on the sidewalk just in front of the Flatiron Building Sam Folwell and Cal Harkness, the Cumberland feudists, shook hands Squaring the Circle.†

In following the trail of O. Henry's men and women through Madison Square you have the choice of many benches. This is not the case when Union Square is introduced in the story of Two Thanksgiving Day Gentlemen.‡ The writer tells you that when Stuffy Pete went to the Square to await the coming of the tall thin old gentleman dressed in black and wearing the old-fashioned kind of glasses that won't stay on the nose—the old gentleman who had been Stuffy's host every Thanksgiving Day for

* See "The Four Million."
† See "The Voice of the City."
‡ See "The Trimmed Lamp."

nine years—he "took his seat on the third bench to
the right as you enter Union Square from the east,
at the walk opposite the fountain." Across Union
Square Hastings Beauchamp Moreley sauntered with
a pitying look at the hundreds that lolled upon the
park benches in The Assessor of Success.* One
evening in the Square Murray and the dismissed police captain Marony were sitting side by side trying
to think of schemes to repair their fallen fortunes.
When opportunity came both acted According to
Their Lights.† The captain was reduced to the point
where, to use his own words, he would "marry the
Empress of China for one bowl of chop suey, commit
murder for a plate of beef stew, steal a wafer from a
waif, or be a Mormon for a bowl of chowder." But
his code of honour he still retained. He would not
"squeal." It is to the other extreme of society that
O. Henry takes us when he deals with Gramercy
Park. All about that private square with its locked
gates are the severe mansions of his aristocrats.
There dwelt Alicia Van Der Pool before she married
Robert Walmesley in The Defeat of the City.‡
A house facing the west side of the park was unques-
tionably the home of the Von der Ruyslings. That
illustrious family had dwelt there for many years.
In fact, in a spirit of obvious awe, O. Henry imparted
the information that the Von der Ruyslings had re-

* See "The Trimmed Lamp."
† See "The Trimmed Lamp."
‡ See "The Voice of the City."

257

ceived the first key ever made to Gramercy Park. In The Marry Month of May* we learn that near the Park old Mr. Coulson had a house, the gout, half a million dollars, a daughter, and a housekeeper. It was the daughter who thought to chill her father's springtime ardour by the introduction of a thousand pounds of ice into the basement. It was the housekeeper that thwarted the scheme with the result that the old millionaire uttered his deferred proposal while Miss Van Meeker Constantia Coulson ran away with the iceman.

VI

GREENWICH VILLAGE

Of all men Sydney Porter was one of the most difficult of approach. To his last day he was shy and almost suspicious of the stranger who was not the casual stranger, that is, the acquaintance scraped in a mood on a bench in Madison Square, or Sheridan Park, or at some corner of "that thoroughfare which parallels and parodies Broadway." There was a little circle of his intimates consisting of such men as Richard Duffy, Gilman Hall, Robert H. Davis, H. Peyton Steger, Robert Rudd Whiting and a few more, to whom he was accessible at any hour of the night or day. But these men knew that it was out of the question to arrange formally a meeting between O. Henry and some one who wanted to know

*See "Whirligigs."

him; knew that at the first hint the quarry would take fright and disappear. So the encounter had to have every appearance of mere chance. Into Porter's rooms on Irving Place or in the Caledonia, where he lived later, the friend would drop, apparently for a word or two of business. With him there would be a stranger, whom the friend had chanced to pick up on the way. Nine times out of ten the friend would not introduce the other two. But after a few minutes' talk and in response to a prearranged signal, the stranger would remark that he had stumbled on a joint near the Bowery, or on upper Broadway, where there was a cocktail mixer who had tended bar in forty-seven cities of the United States. Before the words were out of his mouth Porter had reached for his hat. The friend was forgotten, and arm in arm story-spinner and stranger sallied forth into the night.

The bait thrown out was not always a cocktail mixer and his experiences. "The most picturesque bit of rear tenement that remains in New York." "That was the hint that I used when the nod came," one man who had found O. Henry in the manner suggested told the writer, "and in three minutes we were in the street. I led him down Irving Place to Fourteenth, to Sixth Avenue, past the Jefferson Market Police Court, into Greenwich Village, past Sheridan Park, and down Grove Street to the very end. There, between the front houses, Nos. 10 and 12, there is an opening. Beyond the opening is a triangle, in the middle of which is a tall telegraph pole, and at the back there are three old brick houses, the front windows of which look out diagonally at a wall against which leaves are growing. 'There is a story there,' said Porter, 'a story that suggests an episode in Murger's *Vie de Bohême*, where the grisette at night waters the flowers to keep them alive. The lifetime of the flowers, you remember, was to be the lifetime of that transient love.' He wrote that story, I am sure, in The Last Leaf,* and when I see that bare, dreary yard, and the blank wall of the house twenty feet away, and the old ivy vine, I recall the pathetic tale of Sue and Joanna and the masterpiece that old Behrman painted at the cost of his life."

This Greenwich Village section of the city always appealed strongly to O. Henry's imagination. He liked to picture the odd zigzagging of the streets and to people them with the artists of his creation. Somewhere down in Greenwich Village was the "Vallambrosa" where the self-reliant Hetty lived and furnished the beef for the making of the Irish stew as related in The Third Ingredient.† There, too—in the red brick district, was The Furnished Room,‡ with its suggestion of mignonette. A few blocks away to the south and west is Abingdon Square. In The Thing's the Play,§ we are told "there stands a house near Abingdon Square. On the ground floor

* See "The Trimmed Lamp."
† See "Options."
‡ See "The Four Million."
§ See "Strictly Business."

there has been for twenty-five years a little store where toys and notions and stationery are sold." There Mrs. Frank Barry, deserted on her wedding night on account of a strange misunderstanding, lived out her life awaiting the return of her husband.

Fifth Avenue or First, Riverside Drive or Division Street, Broadway or the Bowery, Corlears Hook Park or Gramercy; no matter what the locality or the social scale of its denizens, it is always Bagdad. And with the night comes the glamour that belongs not to Arabia alone. In different masquerade the streets, bazaars, and walled houses of the Occidental city of romance are filled with the same kind of people that interested Haroun-al-Raschid in his golden prime. Clothes may be different, but underneath men and women are unchanged. With the eye of faith the traveller can see the Little Hunchback, Sinbad the Sailor, Fitbad the Tailor, the Beautiful Persian, the one-eyed Calenders, the Barber and his Six Brothers, and Ali Baba and Forty Robbers on every block.

Many have been the men and the women who have invaded New York as a literary field. But so far there has been but one conqueror of Alexander-like ambitions. And as became a conqueror, he was constantly rechristening the city to suit his own whimsical humour. At one moment it was his "Little Old Bagdad-on-the-Subway," at another, the "City of Too Many Caliphs"; at another, "Noisyville-on-the-Hudson"; or "The Big Town of Razzle-Dazzle"; or, "Wolfville-on-the-Subway"; or, "The City of

Chameleon Changes." Yet Porter discovered New York comparatively late in life; lived in it but the few brief last years. The story has often been told of how, a few minutes before the end came, he whispered to those about him: "Pull up the shades. I don't want to go home in the dark." I like to believe that he did not want to go home without one last glimpse of the town that he had learned to love so well; one last glimpse of his "Little Old Bagdad-on-the-Subway"; his "City of Too Many Caliphs."

O. HENRY AND NEW ORLEANS

By Caroline Francis Richardson

A SETTING that appealed strongly both to O. Henry's story-instinct and to his sympathy, was downtown New Orleans. Like many other writers he found inspiration in the narrow, dingy, shadowy Quarter whose buildings and street names and traditions tell of many things that to-day are lost: riches and lives and causes. But O. Henry used his "copy" differently from other story-tellers who have found suggestion in New Orleans. In the O. Henry tales no plot hinges on a mixture of blood; no hero or heroine is engulfed by flood or devoured by plague; no person speaks an unintelligible dialect. There is no use of Mardi Gras, All Saints' Day, or *quartorze juillet*. And this handling of material is quite characteristic of the author. In all his stories, wherever placed, he makes use of every detail that will add reality to a character or an occurrence. But he does not introduce localities and localisms merely for their intrinsic interest.

As a setting New Orleans can claim but a scant share in the lives of some of O. Henry's knights of high adventure. This is the case with a certain grafter and his partner, Caligula, who of their stay

263

could remember only some drinks "invented by the creoles during the period of Louey Cans, in which they are still served at the side doors"; and an attempt "to make the French Quarter pay up the back trading stamps due on the Louisiana Purchase." It is in that story, Hostages to Momus,* that the Grafter explains the component parts of a perfect breakfast: "There'll never be a perfect breakfast eaten until some man grows arms long enough to stretch down to New Orleans for his coffee and over to Norfolk for his rolls, and reaches up to Vermont and digs a slice of butter out of a spring-house, and then turns over a beehive close to a clover patch out in Indiana for the rest. Then he'd come pretty close to making a meal that the gods eat on Mount Olympus."

Many of these birds of passage merely arrive and depart by way of fruit steamers coming from or going to an explosion in Central America. In that case, the city sees them only while they pick their way over a banana-strewn wharf, dodging the long line of men who pass the green bunches in a swaying chain from the hold of the ship to the freight cars near by. It was by pretending to be a part of such a line that the too sympathetic, too easily won Clancy and the escaping revolutionist, General de Vega, landed undetected from the ship in which they had travelled as stowaways (The Shamrock and the Palm†).

---

* See "The Gentle Grafter."

† See "Cabbages and Kings."

In Lafayette Square Clancy consummated his dark
scheme. With the connivance of a policeman,
a fellow Irishman, the General was arrested as a
vagrant and sentenced to sixty days' hard labour.
The General, be it remembered, had lured Clancy to
Guatemala as a revolutionist, but had forced him to
assist for sixty days in building a railroad. And
now—"Havin' no money, they set him (The General) to work his fine out with a gang from the parish
prison clearing Ursulines Street. Around the corner
was a saloon decorated genially with electric fans
and cool merchandise. I made that me headquarters, and every fifteen minutes I'd walk around
and take a look at the little man fillibustering with a
rake and shovel. . . . Carrambos! Erin go
bragh!"

In Phœbe* a less triumphant Irishman is
shown us: "Bad-luck Kearney." His untoward
adventures reach us through Captain Patricio Maloné, "a Hiberno-Iberian creole," who tells the story
while sitting over cognac in a "little red-tiled café
near Congo Square." From his first sight of Kearney falling into a cellar on Tchoupitoulas Street, the
Captain should have taken warning. But though
Kearney conscientiously declares his handicap, even
leading his new friend out into the middle of the great
width of Canal Street in order to point out the sinister
Saturn and the evil satellite, Phœbe, under which he,
Kearney, was born, Captain Maloné refuses to yield

* See "Roads of Destiny."

to superstition. Later, however, circumstances oblige him to admit the power of the stars, and for the good of the cause, they part. The Captain's conversion is confirmed by his meeting with Kearney a year afterward. On this final occasion Captain Malone, walking near Poydras Market, is brushed aside by "an immensely stout, pink-faced lady in black satin." . . . "Behind her trailed a little man laden to the gunwale with bundles and bags of goods and vegetables." And the little man calls conciliatingly, "I'm coming, Phœbe!"

Very rarely do historic buildings slip into these stories, so it is only as a measure of distance that the old Bourbon Street opera house is used. In A Matter of Mean Elevation,* the reader learns that "The Carabobo Indians are easily the most enthusiastic lovers of music between the equator and the French Opera House in New Orleans." In Blind Man's Holiday,† too, there are buildings we might see on a post card: "the Rue Chartres perishes in the old Place d'Armes. The ancient Cabildo, where Spanish justice fell like hail, faces it, and the Cathedral, another provincial ghost, overlooks it. Its centre is a little iron-railed park. . . . Pedestalled high above it, the general sits his cavorting steed."

In the same story O. Henry makes another departure and yields to the sentiment of French Town:

---

* See "Whirligigs."

† See "Whirligigs."

O. HENRY AND NEW ORLEANS

"The Rue Chartres, in New Orleans, is a street of ghosts. It lies in the quarter where the Frenchman in his prime set up translated pride and glory; where, also, the arrogant don had swaggered, and dreamed of gold grants and ladies' gloves. Every flagstone has its grooves worn by footsteps going royally to the wooing and the fighting. Every house has a princely heartbreak; each doorway its untold tale of gallant promise and slow decay. By night the Rue Chartres is now but a murky fissure, from which the groping wayfarer sees, flung up against the sky, the tangled filigree of Moorish balconies. The old houses of monsieur stand yet, indomitable against the century, but their essence is gone. The street is one of ghosts to whosoever can see them." And in this story is O. Henry's one use of a New Orleans festival: it is on Carnival costumes that Norah Greenway works every and all night—Norah Greenway, the girl who fabricates a past so that her lover, a self-confessed sinner, may have the courage to ask her to marry him.

O. Henry's philosophers of Fortune usually shun hotels. An emphasized instance is that of William Trotter (Helping the Other Fellow*) who comes to New Orleans after a long stay in Aguas Frescas. His brother has offered him a position at a salary of five thousand a year, and expects to meet him at the St. Charles Hotel where they will discuss details. "When I arrived at the Crescent City, I hurried

---

* See "Rolling Stones."

267

away—far away from St. Charles to a dim *chambre garnie* in Bienville Street. And there, looking down from my attic window from time to time at the old absinthe house across the street, I wrote this story to buy my bread and butter."

And it was in "one of those rare old hostelries in Royal Street" that Monsieur Morin lodged—the Monsieur Morin who is so important though unseen a figure in "Cherchez la Femme."* The search for the lady is the self-assumed responsibility of two reporters: Robbins, of the *Picayune*, and Dumars, of *L'Abeille*, "the old French newspaper that has buzzed for nearly a century." In a café in Dumaine Street they argue and conjecture as to M. Morin's disposition of Madame Thibault's twenty thousand dollars, of which he had had the care. The money is finally found in the shape of government bonds carefully pasted by Madame Thibault herself over the unsightly cracks in the wall of one of her rear rooms.

Another native protagonist, in The Renaissance of Charleroi,† is Grandemont Charles, "a little creole gentleman, aged thirty-four, with a bald spot on the top of his head and the manners of a prince. By day he was a clerk in a cotton broker's office in one of those cold, rancid mountains of oozy brick, down near the levee. By night, in the old French Quarter, he was again the last male descendant of the Charles

---

* See "Roads of Destiny."

† See "Roads of Destiny."

family." And in this last character he determines
to spend his painfully saved hoard of six hundred dollars in a renaissance of past glories. He secures the
use of the old plantation house, Charleroi; he fills
it with appropriate furniture, rented from the an-
tique shops in Royal and Chartres streets; he orders
wines and food from famous places—and for an evening, Charleroi lives again. That no one of his invited guests appears, that an uninvited guest does
appear, whose presence means more to Grandemont
than even the glorious past—all this makes it an O.
Henry story.

A plantation below the city is the setting for a
climax in Whistling Dick's Christmas Stocking.*
By means of a freight-car Dick arrives in the "big,
almsgiving, long-suffering city of the South, the cold
weather paradise of tramps." After a cautious survey that includes the levee "pimpled with dark
bulks of merchandise," the long line of Algiers across
the river, the tugs, the ferries, and the Italian luggers,
Dick climbs warily down and starts, whistling, toward
Lafayette Square to meet a pal. But a friendly policeman warns Dick of a new and inhospitable city
ordinance, and he departs hastily for the open road.
A stall keeper in the French Market gives him breakfast, and he is almost happy until Chalmette, with its
"vast and bewildering industry," frightens him and
drives him along a country road hemmed in on one
side by the high green levee and on the other by a

---

*See "The Roads of Destiny."

mysterious, frog-haunted, mosquito-infested marsh.
The incident of a tramp saving a family from burg-
lary and fire, because of a kindly word from a young
girl, is not new; and the plantation house and household are typical and trite. But Whistling Dick is
real. It is entirely logical that after his glorious
evening as honoured guest, and his comfortable night
on the floor of his well-furnished room, he should,
on looking out of the window at the dawn of Christmas Day, feel a distinct shock. He sees and hears
the evidences of the labour that a monster sugar crop
has forced upon a part even of the world holiday.
"Here was a poem; an epic—nay, a tragedy—with
work, the curse of the world, for its theme." A few
moments later Whistling Dick, carefree and happy,
strolls along the top of the levee, away from his grateful hosts, away into the new day and the untram-
melled life.

A SUMMARY OF THE CRITICISM OF TEN YEARS AGO

EVERY reader of current American newspapers and magazines is familiar with the name "O. Henry." It is a pen name, concealing the identity of Mr. Sydney Porter, the author of sundry books of short stories. For some time now his reputation has been steadily growing. Throughout the country are people of all sorts and conditions who agree enthusiastically on one point—that no one else can write short stories like O. Henry's. The critics were at first slow to accept his work. The suggestion that he was "a Yankee Maupassant,"[*] came from his publishers, and did not, for a while, impress the writing fraternity. But now the tables are completely turned. We find William Marion Reedy, of the St. Louis *Mirror*, affirming that, to his thinking, Mr. Porter deserves the very flattering designation conferred upon him; and Henry James Forman, of the editorial staff of the *North American Review*, declares: "He writes with the skill of a Maupassant, and a humour Maupassant never dreamed of." The *Bookman* says, editorially:

---

[*] This appellation is an unconscious tribute to the broad Americanism of a man who lived most of his life in North Carolina and Texas.

271

"While we are inclined to be conservative in the matter of estimating a contemporary writer, and find exceedingly exasperating these impulsive and extravagant recognitions of 'new Stevensons' and 'new Kiplings,' and 'new De Maupassants' and 'American Dickenses,' the time is past for any restraint in the frank appreciation of the work of the author who signs himself 'O. Henry.' The man is in many respects an extraordinary workman and a consummate artist."

The distinguishing characteristics of O. Henry's work are his journalistic style and his democratic instinct. The two combine, as Francis Hackett, the literary editor of the Chicago *Evening Post* points out, in what is distinctly "an original revelation of life." Mr. Hackett says:

"O. Henry writes with a glitter that is characteristic half of the New York *Sun*, half of the *Smart Set*. . . . His scope is restricted. His manner is not discursive. He gets sensational contrasts and assertive colouring into each short story. Allowing for this, he gives us a humorous yet profound understanding of a phase that has not yet been treated before in American art, gives us intimacy with an order of metropolitan characters and circumstances not likely to be better focussed or illumined in our generation.

"O. Henry accepts, with a mixture of irony, wit, and sympathy, the distressing fact that a human being can be a clerk, the remarkable fact that a clerk can

be a human being. He knows the clerk, knows him
in his works and pomps. But there is a peculiarity
in O. Henry's attitude toward the clerk. . . .
Most literary men are intrenched in culture, obfus-
cated by it. They take the uncultured morosely or
pityingly or mordantly. They discuss those who are
not 'élite' as a physician would discuss a case—
scientifically, often humanly, interested, but always
with a strong sense of the case's defects and deficien-
cies.

"To O. Henry, on the contrary, the clerk is neither
abnormal nor subnormal. He writes of him without
patronizing him. He realizes the essential and stu-
pendous truth that to himself the clerk is not pitiable.
He takes into account, in other words, the adjust-
ments that every man makes to constitute himself
the apex of this sphere—for, after all, there are
800,000,000 apices on this sphere, if we dare to assume
that fowl and fishes are not also self-conscious and
self-centred.

"When one says 'clerk' one means $15-a-week
humanity. O. Henry has specialized in this humanity with loving care, with a Kiplingesque attention to
detail. But his is far from the humourless method of
Gissing and Merrick, who were no more happy in
a boarding-house than Thoreau would have been in
the Waldorf-Astoria. O. Henry never forgets the
inherent, the unconscious humour in the paradoxes
and contrasts of mixed civilization, the crudities of
which serve only to exasperate the misplaced and

morbid. He is no moral paradoxist, like Shaw, no
soured idealist, like Zola, no disgruntled esthete,
like Gissing. It is the comedy of the paradoxes
and contrasts that he searches and displays—a comedy in which he miraculously keeps the balance, often
by the adventitious aid of irony and satire, not
sacrificing the clerk to the man of culture, nor, on the
other hand, losing perspective in magnifying the
clerk."

But O. Henry does not confine himself to the clerk.
As Mr. Hackett tells us:

"In one sense Broadway is the spinal column of his
art, and the nerve branches cover all Manhattan.
He knows the side streets where Mamie boards. He
knows Harlem. He knows the narrow-chested flat.
He knows the Bowery, Irish and Yiddish. He knows
the Tenderloin, cop, panhandler, man about town,
sport, bartender, and waiter. He knows Shanley's
and Childs's, the lemon-odoured buffet and the French
table d'hôte. He knows the sham Bohemia, the real
Bohemia. And his stories are starred with little
vignettes of the town, paragraphs of unostentatious
art that let us see Madison Square, or the White
Way, or the Park (over and over again the Park), or
the side street in springtime—all clear as the vision
in the crystal.

"O. Henry's triumphs are often triumphs of fancy.
He has the sense of the marvellous which belongs to
tellers of the short story since the nights of Arabia.
And O. Henry can discover in Manhattan the wonder

of fable and adventure, the eternal symbols of imagination, the beauty of the jewel in the toad."

To this should be added the tribute of William
Marion Reedy:

"As a depicter of the life of New York's four million—club men, fighters, thieves, policemen, touts,
shop-girls, lady cashiers, hoboes, actors, stenog-
raphers, and what not—O. Henry has no equal for
keen insight into the beauties and meannesses of
character or motive. Mordant though he be at
times his heart is with innocence and right, but he
sees the fun that underlies sophistication and selfishness. Not only does he see life, but he sees its prob-
lems and in a certain shy-sly way suggests his solu-
tions therefor. His gifts of description are of a surprising variety in method. His pictures, mostly
small, intimate greater scopes and deeper vistas.
Afraid of pathos, his very promptness to avoid it
upon its slightest hint of imminence gives poignancy
to the note he thus strikes as by suggestion. He loves
the picaroon and the vagabond, and dowers them
with vocabularies rich and strange and fanciful.
. . . He always has a story. The style or the
mood may lure you away from it momentarily, but
the tale always asserts its primacy, and its end comes
always in just the whimsical way you didn't expect.
O. Henry is inexhaustible in quip, in imagery, in
quick, sharp, spontaneous invention. In his ap-
parent carelessness we suspect a carefulness, but this
is just wherein he is sib to the French short-story

writers, chief among them De Maupassant. Della Cruscan critics may disapprove of him for his slang, but until you know his slang, you never know what a powerful vehicle slang can be in the hands of one who can mate it with the echoes from and essences of true literary expression. It is not the slang of George Ade, or Henry M. Blossom, or George V. Hobart. Henry's slang has some of the savour that we find in the archaic vocabulary invented for himself by Chatterton. Its content transcends the capacity of the mere argot of the street. In the American short story to-day O. Henry has demonstrated himself a delightful master, one absolutely unapproachable in swift visualization and penetrative interpretation of life, as any and all of the books now to his credit will show to any one capable of understanding."

O. HENRY'S SHORT STORIES

By Henry James Forman

MR. SYDNEY PORTER, the gentleman who, in the language of some of his characters, is "denounced" by the euphonious pen name of O. Henry, has breathed new life into the short story. Gifted as he is with a flashing wit, abundant humour, and quick observation, no subject has terrors for him. If it be too much to say, in the old phrase, that nothing human is alien to him, at least the larger part of humanity is his domain. The very title of one of his books, "The Four Million," is a protest against those who believe that New York contains only four hundred people worth while. O. Henry backs the census-taker against the social arbiter. The rich and the fashionable are, in his tales, conceived much in the spirit of similar characters in melodrama, except that the ingredient of humour is put in to mitigate them. Indeed, they figure but seldom. But the poor and the lowly, the homeless lodger of the city park, the vagabond of the "bread line," the waitress, the shop and factory girl, the ward politician, the city policeman, the whole "ruck and rabble" of life, so meaningless to the comfortable, unobservant bourgeois, are set forth always with keen knowledge, with a laughing humour, and not infrequently with a tender, smiling pathos. As this panorama of the undenoted faces of the great city passes before the reader, he becomes his own Caliph Haroun-al-Raschid, and New York a teeming Bagdad, full of romance and mystery.

The facility, the light touch of O. Henry, his mastery of the vernacular, his insight into the life of the disinherited, make it needless for him to resort to such inventions as Stevenson's learned Arabian, imaginary author of the "New Arabian Nights." The piquant and picturesque phrasing, the dash of slang, the genial and winning fancy seem to carry off the most fantastic situations. The Touchstone, the jester, the merry-maker has always enjoyed a certain license if he had but the wit not to abuse it. O. Henry's fun is never of the slapstick variety and his pathos never bathos.

We are shaken with sad laughter at the many and divers attempts of the park-bench vagabond, Soapy,* to be arrested and sent to the workhouse for the winter months. He eats a meal and does not pay, he steals an umbrella, he accosts unescorted women, but all to no purpose. The police seem to regard him "as a king who could do no wrong." But as he passes by a church the organ music of an anthem vividly recalls his boyhood, stirs the tramp to his depths, and he resolves to turn over a new leaf. He will seek work and be a man. Then the policeman

---

* The Cop and the Anthem, in "The Four Million."

lays a hand upon him, hales him before a magistrate as a vagrant, and the city's swirling machinery of the law sends Soapy to "the Island" after all. And the author smiles with tender compassion over this poor shuttlecock of fate.

With no less humorous kindness does he deal with 'Tildy, "the unwooed drudge," the plain little waitress in an Eighth Avenue chop-house.* All the hurrying *clientèle* of that eating-house admired Aileen, who "was tall, beautiful, lively, gracious, and learned in persiflage." But no one had a word for 'Tildy of the freckles and the hay-coloured hair, until one day a tipsy laundry clerk put his arm round 'Tildy's waist and kissed her. For a brief space that transformed her life. 'Tildy the unnoticed began to bind ribbons in her hair, to prink and to preen after the fashion of daughters of Eve. "A gentleman insulted me to-day," she modestly informed all her customers. "He put his arm around my waist and kissed me." And as the diners turned upon her the stream of badinage hitherto directed at Aileen alone, 'Tildy's heart swelled in her bosom, "for she saw at last the towers of Romance rise above the horizon of the gray plain in which she had for so long travelled." 'Tildy had a thrilling sensation of fear lest Seeders, the laundry clerk, in a mood of jealous love-madness, rush in and shoot her with a pistol. This she deplored, for no one had shot Aileen for love, and she did not wish to overshadow her friend. When Seeders does come in

* The Brief Début of Tildy, in "The Four Million."

it is only to apologize, with the plea that he was tipsy. 'Tildy's towers of romance crumble to earth. The glory fades suddenly, for it was not love at all that actuated Seeders. But Aileen the staunch-hearted comforts 'Tildy in her sorrow, for if Seeders "were any kind of a gentleman," she tells her, "he wouldn't of apologized."

"The Trimmed Lamp" is of a piece with "The Four Million," filled with the tragi-comedy of life much as it appeared to Dickens and to François Villon. In "Heart of the West" the author exploits a vein many have attempted in a short story as well as in the novel—the so-called "wild West." But no one, it is safe to say, has brought so much fun and humour to the Western story. Cattle-king, cowboy, miner, the plains and the chaparral—material of the "dime novel," but all treated with the skill of a Maupassant, and a humour Maupassant never dreamed of. The merest sketch of them has a certain substance to it. Yet it is idle to compare O. Henry with anybody. No talent could be more original or more delightful. The combination of technical excellence with whimsical, sparkling wit, abundant humour, and a fertile invention is so rare that the reader is content without comparisons.

O. HENRY INDEX

A

ACCORDING TO THEIR LIGHTS. *See:* Trimmed Lamp, The.

ADJUSTMENT OF NATURE, AN. *See:* Four Million, The.

ADMIRAL, THE. *See:* Cabbages and Kings.

ADVENTURES IN NEURASTHENIA. *Same as* Let Me Feel Your Pulse.

ADVENTURES OF SHAMROCK JOLNES, THE. *See:* Sixes and Sevens.

AFTER THE BATTLE. *Same as* The Crucible.

AFTER TWENTY YEARS. *See:* Four Million, The.

AFTERNOON MIRACLE, AN. *See:* Heart of the West.

ALIAS JIMMY VALENTINE. *Dramatization of* Retrieved Reformation, A.

APOLOGY, AN. *See:* Rolling Stones.

ARISTOCRACY VERSUS HASH. *See:* Rolling Stones.

ART AND THE BRONCO. *See:* Roads of Destiny.

ASSESSOR OF SUCCESS, THE. *See:* Trimmed Lamp, The.

AT ARMS WITH MORPHEUS. *See:* Sixes and Sevens.

ATAVISM OF JOHN TOM LITTLE BEAR, THE. *See:* Rolling Stones.

ATWOOD, JOHNNY. *See:* Note under Cabbages and Kings.

B

BABES IN THE JUNGLE. *See:* Strictly Business.

BADGE OF POLICEMAN O'ROON, THE. *See:* Trimmed Lamp, The.

BEST-SELLER. *See:* Options.

BETWEEN ROUNDS. *See:* Four Million, The.

BEXAR SCRIPT, No. 2692. *See:* Rolling Stones.

BIRD OF BAGDAD, A. *See:* Strictly Business.

BLACKJACK BARGAINER, A. *See:* Whirligigs.

BLIND MAN'S HOLIDAY. *See:* Whirligigs.

BRICKDUST ROW. *See:* Trimmed Lamp, The.

BRIEF DÉBUT OF 'TILDY, THE. *See:* Four Million, The.

BURIED TREASURE. *See:* Options.

BUYER FROM CACTUS CITY. THE. *See:* Trimmed Lamp, The.

BY COURIER. *See:* Four Million, The.

C

CABALLERO'S WAY, THE. *See:* Heart of the West.

CABBAGES AND KINGS.

The stories in this volume, though apparently disconnected chapters, fall into four main groups, with the exception of one independent tale, The Lotus and the Bottle. But the stories all have a loose inter-relation owing to the fact that Coralio in Central America is their common stage, and that the *dramatis personæ*, generally speaking, is the same throughout. For the advantage of readers who wish to get the chapters of the various stories in their natural order, the groups are here marked alphabetically. For instance, all the chapters centring about Frank Goodwin are grouped with The Money Maze as A. Those about Johnny Atwood with Cupid's Exile Number Two as B. Those about Keogh and Clancy with The Phonograph and the Graft as C. Those about Dicky as D and those about The Admiral as E.

CONTENTS:

The Proem: By the Carpenter, A

"Fox-in-the-Morning," A

The Lotus and the Bottle

Smith, A

Caught, A

Cupid's Exile Number Two, B

O. HENRY INDEX

O. HENRY INDEX

E

F

CONTENTS:

The Cop and the Anthem
An Adjustment of Nature
Memoirs of a Yellow Dog
The Love-Philtre of Ikey Schoenstein
Mammon and the Archer
Springtime à la Carte
The Green Door
From the Cabby's Seat
An Unfinished Story
The Caliph, Cupid and the Clock
Sisters of the Golden Circle
The Romance of a Busy Broker
After Twenty Years
Lost on Dress Parade
By Courier
The Furnished Room
The Brief Début of 'Tildy

G

GENTLE GRAFTER, THE (ILLUSTRATED)—SHORT STORIES.

CONTENTS:

The Octopus Marooned
Jeff Peters as a Personal Magnet
Modern Rural Sports
The Chair of Philanthromathematics
The Hand that Riles the World
The Exact Science of Matrimony
A Midsummer Masquerade
Shearing the Wolf
Innocents of Broadway
Conscience in Art
The Man Higher Up
A Tempered Wind
Hostages to Momus
The Ethics of Pig

O. HENRY INDEX

O. HENRY INDEX

CONTENTS:

I

J

K

L

O. HENRY INDEX

Locality

A geographical arrangement of practically all of the stories.   Reference to the book in which the tale appears is given after each title or group of titles.

Central America

England

O. HENRY INDEX

291

O. HENRY INDEX

Transformation of Martin Burney }
The Caliph and the Cad } *In* Sixes and Sevens
The Diamond of Kali }

"Strictly Business." (All the stories in this volume, except "A Municipal Report," for which see THE SOUTH under *Tennessee*.)

"The Trimmed Lamp." (Whole volume)

"The Voice of the City." (Whole volume)

Calloway's Code }
"Girl" }
The Marry Month of May }
Sociology in Serge and Straw }
Suite Homes and Their Romance }
A Sacrifice Hit } *In* Whirligigs
The Song and the Sergeant }
A Newspaper Story }
Tommy's Burglar }
A Little Local Colour }

Pennsylvania (*Pittsburgh*)

Conscience in Art. (*In* Whirligigs)

South America

"Cabbages and Kings." (Whole volume)

The World and the Door }
The Theory and the Hound }
A Matter of Mean Elevation } *In* Options
Supply and Demand }

Next to Reading Matter }
A Double-Dyed Deceiver } *In* Roads of Destiny
On Behalf of the Management }

A Ruler of Men }
Helping the Other Fellow } *In* Rolling Stones

THE SOUTH—

Alabama

The Ransom of Red Chief. (*In* Whirligigs)

292

O. HENRY INDEX

O. HENRY INDEX

Arkansas

Jeff Peters as a Personal Magnet ⎱ *In* The Gentle Grafter
The Man Higher Up. ⎰

A Retrieved Reformation.   (*In* Roads of Destiny)

Colorado

The Ransom of Mack.   (*In* Heart of the West)
The Friendly Call.   (*In* Rolling Stones`

Illinois

The Exact Science of Matrimony.   (*In* The Gentle Grafter)

Indiana

Modern Rural Sports.   (*In* The Gentle Grafter)

Indian Territory

New York by Campfire Light.   (*In* Sixes and Sevens)
A Technical Error.   (*In* Whirligigs)

Kansas

The Atavism of John Tom Little Bear.   (*In* Rolling Stones)

Montana

The Handbook of Hymen.   (*In* Heart of the West)

New Mexico

Telemachus Friend.   (*In* Heart of the West)

Oklahoma

Cupid à la Carte.   (*In* Heart of the West)
Holding Up a Train.   (*In* Sixes and Sevens)

Texas

The Octopus Marooned.   (*In* The Gentle Grafter)
Hearts and Crosses ⎫
The Pimienta Pancakes ⎪
Seats of the Haughty ⎬ *In* Heart of the West
Hygeia at the Solito ⎭

294

O. HENRY INDEX

295

O. HENRY INDEX

O. HENRY INDEX

PLUTONIAN FIRE, THE. *See:* Voice of the City, The.
POEMS BY O. HENRY. *See:* Rolling Stones.

Titles:

The Pewee.
Nothing to Say.
The Murderer.
Some Postscripts.
Two Portraits.
A Contribution.
The Old Farm.

Vanity.
The Lullaby Boy.
Chanson de Bohême.
Hard to Forget.
Drop a Tear in this Slot.
Tamales.

POET AND THE PEASANT, THE. *See:* Strictly Business.

POOR RULE, A. *See:* Options.

PORTER FAMILY, RECORD OF BIRTHS AND DEATHS. *See:* Rolling Stones.

PORTRAITS OF O. HENRY AT VARIOUS AGES. *See:* Rolling Stones.

PRIDE OF THE CITIES, THE. *See:* Sixes and Sevens.

PRINCESS AND THE PUMA, THE. *See:* Heart of the West.

PRISONER OF ZEMBLA, THE. *See:* Rolling Stones.

PROEM, THE: BY THE CARPENTER. *See:* Cabbages and Kings.

PROOF OF THE PUDDING. *See:* Strictly Business.

PSEUDONYMS USED BY O. HENRY: Olivier Henry; S. H. Peters; James L. Bliss; T. B. Dowd; and Howard or Harry Clark.

PSYCHE AND THE PSKYSCRAPER. *See:* Strictly Business.

PURPLE DRESS, THE. *See:* Trimmed Lamp, The.

Q

QUERIES AND ANSWERS. *See:* Rolling Stones.

QUEST OF SOAPY. *Same as* The Cop and the Anthem.

R

RAGGLES. *Same as* Making of a New Yorker, The.

RAMBLE IN APHASIA, A. *See:* Strictly Business.

RANSOM OF MACK, THE. *See:* Heart of the West.

RANSOM OF RED CHIEF, THE. (*To be dramatized*). *See:* Whirligigs.

RATHSKELLER AND THE ROSE, THE. *See:* Voice of the City, The.

RED ROSES OF TONIA. *See:* Waifs and Strays.

REFORMATION OF CALLIOPE, THE. *See:* Heart of the West.

REMNANTS OF THE CODE, THE. *See:* Cabbages and Kings.

RENAISSANCE AT CHARLEROI, THE. *See:* Roads of Destiny.

REPRODUCTIONS OF MANUSCRIPT AND PAGES FROM THE PLUNKVILLE PATRIOT AS PRINTED BY O. HENRY IN THE ROLLING STONE. *See:* Rolling Stones.

RETRIEVED REFORM. *Same as* Retrieved Reformation, A.

RETRIEVED REFORMATION, A. (*Dramatized as* "Alias Jimmy Valentine.") *See:* Roads of Destiny.

ROADS OF DESTINY—SHORT STORIES.

CONTENTS:

Roads of Destiny (*To be dramatized*)
The Guardian of the Accolade
The Discounters of Money
The Enchanted Profile
"Next to Reading Matter"
Art and the Bronco
Phœbe
A Double-Dyed Deceiver
The Passing of Black Eagle
A Retrieved Reformation
Cherchez la Femme
Friends in San Rosario

The Fourth in Salvador
The Emancipation of Billy
The Enchanted Kiss
A Departmental Case
The Renaissance at Charleroi
On Behalf of the Management
Whistling Dick's Christmas Stocking
The Halberdier of the Little Rheinschloss
Two Renegades
The Lonesome Road

O. HENRY INDEX

O. HENRY INDEX

An Unfinished Christmas Story
The Unprofitable Servant—Unfinished
Aristocracy versus Hash (from *The Rolling Stone*)
The Prisoner of Zembla (from *The Rolling Stone*)
A Strange Story (from *The Rolling Stone*)
Fickle Fortune or How Gladys Hustled (from *The Rolling Stone*)
An Apology (from *The Rolling Stone*)
Lord Oakhurst's Curse (sent in a letter to Dr. Beall, Greensboro, N. C., in 1883)
Bexar Scrip No. 2692 (from *The Rolling Stone*)
Queries and Answers (from *The Rolling Stone*)

Poems:

The Pewee
Nothing to Say
The Murderer
Some Postscripts
  A Contribution
The Old Farm

Vanity
The Lullaby Boy
Chanson de Bohême
Hard to Forget
Drop a Tear in this Slot
Tamales

Letters

Some Letters

O. HENRY INDEX

S

SACRIFICE HIT, A.   *See:* Whirligigs.

SCHOOLS AND SCHOOLS.   *See:* Options.

SEATS OF THE HAUGHTY.   *See:* Heart of the West.

SERVICE OF LOVE, A.   *See:* Four Million, The.

SHAMROCK AND THE PALM, THE.   *See:* Cabbages and Kings.

SHAMROCK JOLNES.

> A character occurring in The Sleuths and also in The Adventures of Shamrock Jolnes.   *See:* Sixes and Sevens

SHEARING THE WOLF.   *See:* Gentle Grafter, The.

SHIPS.   *See:* Cabbages and Kings.

SHOCKS OF DOOM, THE.   *See:* Voice of the City, The.

SHOES.   *See:* Cabbages and Kings.

SISTERS OF THE GOLDEN CIRCLE.   *See:* Four Million, The.

SIXES AND SEVENS—SHORT STORIES.

CONTENTS:

SKYLIGHT ROOM, THE.   *See:* Four Million, The.

SLEUTHS, THE.   *See:* Sixes and Sevens.

SMITH. *See:* Cabbages and Kings.

SNAPSHOT AT THE PRESIDENT, A. *See:* Rolling Stones.

SNOW MAN, THE. *See:* Waifs and Strays.

SOCIAL TRIANGLE, THE. *See:* Trimmed Lamp, The.

SOCIOLOGY IN SERGE AND STRAW. *See:* Whirligigs.

SONG AND THE SERGEANT, THE. *See:* Whirligigs.

SOUND AND FURY—DIALOGUE. *See:* Rolling Stones.

SOUTH AMERICA, STORIES OF. *See:* Locality.

SOUTH, STORIES OF THE. *See:* Locality.

SPARROWS IN MADISON SQUARE, THE. *See:* Waifs and Strays.

SPHINX APPLE, THE. *See:* Heart of the West.

SPRINGTIME À LA CARTE. *See:* Four Million, The.

SQUARING THE CIRCLE. *See:* Voice of the City, The.

STEGER, H. P.

> O. Henry's personal friend who edited Rolling Stones and wrote the introduction to the last collection of his works. *See:* Rolling Stones.

STICKNEY'S NECKTIE. *Same as* Unfinished Christmas Story.

STRANGE STORY, A. *See:* Rolling Stones.

STRICTLY BUSINESS—SHORT STORIES.

CONTENTS:

Strictly Business	A Municipal Report
The Gold That Glittered	Psyche and the Pskyscraper
Babes in the Jungle	A Bird of Bagdad
The Day Resurgent	Compliments of the Season
The Fifth Wheel	
The Poet and the Peasant	A Night in New Arabia
The Robe of Peace	The Girl and the Habit
The Girl and the Graft	Proof of the Pudding
The Call of the Tame	Past One at Rooney's
The Unknown Quantity	The Venturers
The Thing's the Play	The Duel
A Ramble in Aphasia	"What You Want"

O. HENRY INDEX

Successful Political Intrigue, A. *See:* Tictocq in Rolling Stones.

Suite Homes and Their Romance. *See:* Whirligigs.

Supply and Demand. *See:* Options.

T

Tainted Tenner, The Tale of a. *See:* Trimmed Lamp, The.

Technical Error, A. *See:* Whirligigs.

Telemachus, Friend. *See:* Heart of the West.

Tempered Wind, A. *See:* Gentle Grafter, The.

Texas, Stories of. *See:* Locality, Stories of the West.

Thanksgiving Day Gentlemen, Two. *See:* Trimmed Lamp, The.

Theory and the Hound, The. *See:* Whirligigs.

Thimble, Thimble. *See:* Options.

Thing's the Play, The. *See:* Strictly Business.

Third Ingredient, The. (*Has been dramatized.*) *See:* Options.

Tictocq.

> Two French Detective Stories
> A Successful Political Intrigue
> Tracked to Doom
> *See:* Rolling Stones

To Him Who Waits. *See:* Options.

Tobin's Palm. *See:* Four Million, The.

Tommy's Burglar. *See:* Whirligigs.

Tracked to Doom, or the Mystery of the Rue De Peychaud. *See:* Rolling Stones.

Transformation of Martin Burney, The. *See:* Sixes and Sevens.

Transients in Arcadia. *See:* Voice of the City, The.

Trimmed Lamp, The—Short Stories.

O. HENRY INDEX

CONTENTS: